Memoirs of a Mongol without a Pony

R. G. Stern

Banal Press   Tucson, Arizona

This edition was prepared for publication by
Ghost River Images
5350 East Fourth Street
Tucson, Arizona 85711
www.ghostriverimages.com

Front cover photo © D. L. Stern
Back cover photo © R. G. Stern

Library of Congress Control Number: 2016903395

ISBN 978-0-692-65322-7

Printed in the United States of America

First Printing: March, 2016

10 9 8 7 6 5 4 3 2 1

This book is dedicated to the memory of my father, Henry Stern, who died when he and I were young, but lived an extraordinarily long life in my heart and mind.

Also by R. G. Stern

ORB: A Contemporary Fable

Contents

Preface

Though inspired by real events and people, this book should be considered a work of fiction.

That's because my memory of things is imprecise and I simply can't remember every detail exactly as it happened. I didn't keep a diary. Actually, only a few parts of it are fiction and most parts are absolute fact, but there is enough overlap that even I can't remember exactly where I had to 'fill in the blanks' to move the story along. So let's call it all fiction for legal purposes. It is intended to reflect a life in the same way one can see reflections in water. That is, some images are real, some are mirrored, and others are purposefully distorted by small pebbles thrown across the surface. Sometimes even boulders. Now is that a poetic description or what? When well known names appear, these are real events and people, but the representations should be considered fictitious in that literary license was taken. In any event, named people are hopefully cast in positive terms, consistent with their fine character, importance to the story and the life depicted. For those individuals cast in darkness, names and identities have been changed, not to protect them (for who should be protected from the truthful written word), but mostly to avoid even mentioning their names, which still cause considerable gastric distress to this day. Fortunately, the balance sheet strongly favors the good folk.

Introduction

My name is Shane. I was named after a cowboy movie that is very famous starring Alan Ladd. I don't think anyone under 60 years of age has heard of it anymore, thus it really is not that famous. I saw it once and I have to say it didn't do much for me. Apparently, it didn't do much for my mom, who says it was a nothing special western and that the character named Shane wore a really silly leather fringed cowboy outfit. She just saw the movie the night before I popped out and simply liked the name. In those days, Shane was a very uncommon name and I don't meet many people my age who have it. Then it became popular for a while so there's a whole bunch of 20 and 30 year olds who have it. I liked it better when I had it to myself for the most part. No confusion in school classes and things like that.

I have what is medically known as Down syndrome, an increasingly chic and popular genetic disorder in contemporary Western society. Popular in the sense that Down's people are sort of cute (they even have Down's fashion models now, some of whom are pretty hot), are seemingly happy-go-lucky, and are not prone to dramatic outbursts of temper or violence as are other supposedly disabled people.

Or the general population for that matter, which seem to have that affliction to a far greater degree. A lot of us are a bit overweight (not me–I am very slim and fit), but for unknown reasons we are not looked down upon for chubbiness as much as 'normal' folks. Likely an issue of relativity.

I imagine some readers are going to be put off by the title of my book. My parents say it is politically incorrect, but I will try to explain it from my point of view. We used to be called Mongoloid a lot, and sometimes still are, especially by people from Mississippi. Which is not surprising since I heard that the people in that state have the worst public education in the country, sort of like special education for the whole population. That's an interesting educational experiment when you think about it. I'm guessing that the whole mongoloid thing started because, presumably, we look like Mongols. But I've seen some movies from Mongolia and let me tell you something. First, we don't even remotely look like Mongols–we each have some very attractive features, but they are different. Those Mongols should be pretty pissed off being compared to supposedly mentally deficient people–what an insult to them, for no apparent reason. They live in these great round tents called yurts, ride around on beautiful ponies, have close, funny families and seem very happy. Course, those Mongols and yurts are in movies, so you never know. I asked my dad once, if we could go camping and get one of those great tents. He looked at me and rolled his eyes like he always does when I have a great idea that would cost him some cash. But I still can't figure out why Americans like to insult them–I think they need a version of the American Down Syndrome Society–they could call it the American Society for Mongols Who Don't Have Down Syndrome. Admittedly, they wouldn't have a large following, given the hostility they've endured all these years. And I don't see a lot of Mongols when we go out eating and drinking. But it wouldn't hurt to try.

I'm not going to tell you my entire life story, because who can remember all that. And correctly, too. Autobiographies and biographies are way over-rated, very biased and inaccurate. They try to give a beginning, middle and end to an entire life and seamlessly integrate everything into a neat complete whole. Well, life is a mess, hopefully a good mess. My book is a story of excerpts and anecdotes from a life well lived (how pathetically trite a phrase–an example of my dad's literary limitations), and it is up to the reader to put them all together coherently. I still haven't figured it out, other than the fact I have had a blast so far. But before I launch into my patchwork story of the essentials of my life, I need to warn you about a few interesting things that you will notice if you continue reading.

The first is that I curse a fair amount. That's because of my parents, who also curse a lot. I only know 4 or 5 really good cuss words, but since my general vocabulary is so limited, it is only natural that my cussing vocabulary is similarly limited. If it bothers you, contact some child welfare agency. I've actually done that myself, as well as report my parents to the Philadelphia Police Department for locking me in a cage every night, but you'll have to read on to learn those details. When I first started in school, they kept calling my parents about my cursing, which was apparently a big problem for all the other kids and the teachers. What they didn't understand was that my parents taught me to curse appropriately, politely, and 'expressively'. I haven't a fucking clue what that means, but I think I got it right. It means that if you slam your finger in a door, it is perfectly fine to scream 'motherfucker', shake your finger and move on. Or when your favorite basketball player slams a great dunk, you say "Holy Shit!", that was badass. But you never say a curse word against another person for no reason, unless they deserve it. Like if someone tries to knock you down and take your money in the school bathroom, it's perfectly fine to say 'fuck off' and defend yourself. The rules are pretty self-explanatory. So I am not apologizing for my cuss words and if they offend you, tough shit, don't read the book. Fair warning.

This book was essentially dictated to my parents and written primarily by my father who is a well-known bullshit artist for his entire life. Fact is, there are only about 10–15 people in the world that can understand most of what I say. Fortunately, most of my cuss words are only one syllable, so almost everyone gets those right away. I am hard of hearing with a significant speech impediment, but I am not an idiot. Many of the people who bend over and talk baby-shit talk to me are idiots, but I am not one of them. Though I easily make myself clear to family and close friends, I often have to resort to alternative means of expression for those less familiar with my 'patois' (another ridiculous term my father chose). This has made me a master of charades, hand gestures, a bit of signing, bizarre facial expressions, writing half-legible words, freeze framing TV's and computers to show people what I am talking about or what I want and other such nonsense. It's a pain in the ass, cause I have a lot to say, and I am well aware I am not getting through to most people. Especially babes, but that is a matter I will touch on later. But I couldn't have written this book by myself and it suffers accordingly. Whenever there are obscure philosophical digressions that are removed from the real storyline–my storyline, that is my parents' attempt to infiltrate the primary discourse with their own rhetoric and philosophical musings–this entire sentence being a prime example of their corrupting influence on the matter at hand. When these moments occur, I will sometimes point them out to readers in parentheses as a sort of disavowal, but in general, this will be obvious to you. Such is one of my handicaps, to be at the mercy of biased, self-indulgent storytellers who I must rely upon to assist me in telling MY story. Some handicaps are not easily appreciated.

My dad says this is a rambling, sometimes repetitive, and grammatically incorrect autobiography. He says I keep changing verb tenses, the punctuation sucks, and I use the same descriptive words too many times. He says we need an editor and he has some friends who are editors who could fix up the sentences and 'structure' of the book better than him. I told him I didn't want some other person telling my story, cause I'm already pissed off I even have to rely on him to tell my story. I simply told him that was his job, but he said there wasn't a lot he could do if I insisted on dictating my stories to him in this disorganized manner. Which I did insist upon, since it's my goddam story. And I love using dashes and dots everywhere. I told him not to worry about it. It's not like we are going to make a living at this.

Finally, the episodes described in this book depict both good and bad behavior on my part, often funny, since I am a clown by nature, but sometimes I did bad. Not really harmful bad, but bad enough to piss people off. For instance, I am truly sorry for the small race riot that I caused in elementary school, but as you will learn later, I am neither racist nor colorblind. For the good things, I claim personal credit. For all the times I used bad judgment, I politely but sincerely attribute this to my upbringing. That is what parents are for.

The Florida Years

Chapter 1
Scaring people at the swimming pool

I learned to swim at an early age.

Yeah, I know. Learning to swim isn't exactly the place one would start a memoir, but I have had an unusual life and it turns out I began my swimming lessons at about two weeks of age. This would be my mother's idea, of course. I have no recollection of the process and have to rely on the history related to me by the usual questionable sources.

I was a big time premie and didn't even walk until I was around 4 years of age, but my mother was determined that I would be a good swimmer, likely because she was a great swimmer and diver. Funny how people want their kids to be like them. Perhaps her intentions were noble, but I fear her main concern was that if I became a strong swimmer quickly, she wouldn't have to watch me very closely when I was at the apartment complex pool. In her defense, she didn't start drinking alcohol until much later in life and was generally attentive to me–I don't remember a lot of sunburns.

She says she started by dunking me a lot in the bathtub. She wasn't a big believer in baby tubs. She was the real deal–took me straight into the big bathtub with her, with me laying on her belly and gently submerging me along with herself for brief periods so I learned to hold my breath the instant the water hit my mouth. I think this is instinctive, but there's no reason to crush the illusions of well-intentioned parents who think they replaced the natural course of things. Anyway, several things ultimately evolved from this process. First, I have always loved taking baths, though not so much with my mother as I got older. That's a little creepy. And sure enough, I became a strong swimmer for life. But what I really excelled in was holding my breath. I don't know exactly what she was doing in that bathtub—maybe she was sitting on me—but at a very early age I could hold my breath easily for over a minute and later on for 2 to 3 minutes. We're talking at age 2 months or so to start. Not bad for a handicapper.

It didn't take long for my mom to get comfortable with me in the pool by myself, though I happen to know she watched me like a hawk out of the corner of her eye. She says we practiced a little routine she worked up on weekday early evenings when the apartment complex pool was quiet. She really enjoyed scaring the shit out of other people poolside when we lived in Florida, especially the ones who stared at me like a freak. You gotta remember, this was back in the mid 1970's and staring was the norm for me. So on crowded weekends, she would dress me up in my one-piece swimsuit that looked like it came from the 1890's and she would lug her bag, towels, food, drinks, and me to the complex pool. Supposedly, the first time there were 50 -75 people oiled up in the sun on the poolside chairs or drifting around in the pool. Then she slowly walked all the way around the pool from the shallow end to the deep end carrying me like a sack of potatoes by the back of my suit with my arms and legs stretched out like I was a flying turtle. When she reached the edge of the deep end, she nonchalantly dropped me into the water whereupon I immediately sank to the bottom and calmly sat, holding my breath. People started yelling and screaming at her, but she casually wandered away to find a nearby set of chairs for us to settle into. I just loved sitting on the bottom holding my breath–I truly think I remember that because I've done it my whole life. I just don't float–probably too little body fat or something. I can do 20 consecutive flips underwater right now in early middle age, but I still can't float–just sink to the bottom. Anyway, for the first few times she dropped me in the deep end as a baby and several weeks thereafter, people would dive in to rescue me and bring me up to the surface and start screaming at her. I think they even threatened to call the police or so I am told. She would just calmly smile and say, "He's just swimming and enjoying the pool, like all the other children."

And the rescuer(s) would say, "No, he wasn't swimming, he was just drowning at the bottom. He can't swim. Just look at him down there. Are you nuts, lady?"

And she would smile sweetly and answer, "Why don't you worry about your own children and I will worry about my child. He is just fine. And by the way, it's none of your fucking business."

My mom never gets in arguments much. She says things so calmly that it disables people. And those people always backed off pretty quickly.

Apparently there was never a more pronounced argument because as soon as I was given back to her, she would walk over to the edge of the pool and drop me back in. The second time, all eyes were on me and I must have known it, since my mother said she even started getting nervous at about 2 minutes or so, but then I would paddle my way to the surface and over to the side of the pool and asked to be dropped in again. I loved it. We would do this over and over (I remember it when I got a little older) until we both became bored and took naps and then ate–and being the rebel that she was, I didn't have to wait 2 hours after eating before going back in the pool. My dad was usually at work and generally missed out on the circus, but he already knew I was good in the water, so on those occasions when he was there, he just beamed with pride. He's a strange looking dude and no one ever bothered him about my swimming efforts. I mean he wasn't big and tough or anything like that, just strange enough with long hair, beard, dark sunglasses that seemed permanently attached to his head and an obliviousness that kept people at a distance. I don't know the word obliviousness (obviously), but I sure as hell know my dad is an airhead who has the attention span of a fly. Sometimes I think they stared more at him than me, which really boosted my confidence later in life. I'm pretty sure they all thought our entire family was sort of strange. Unfortunately word spread quickly at the apartment complex and the shock value disappeared after a few weeks so that people became so used to me sitting on the bottom of the pool that I became sort of a pool ornament. I never really got to swim and play with the other kids at this age because I was still a freak and truth be told, I couldn't even stand on my two feet yet in the shallow end. But those other little kids wouldn't have dreamed of going to the deep end. My first moral victory and I didn't even know it.

Chapter 2
Banging your head on the floor can be a good thing

As you may have surmised from the swimming story, I never really had a good set of wheels, even from birth. Never could run fast, jump high, and frankly, I never even liked to walk, let alone run. Still don't to this very day. Gimme a cab any day. Even those smelly subways are better than walking in fresh air. I don't like to hike, take neighborhood strolls, walk for errands. This led to some problems later on, but I'll get to that later. But despite my distaste for walking, I did my fair share anyway, when it was in my interest.

The legs are overrated. It's all about upper body strength–you can wear pants to hide your sticks. And relative to the rest of my stickly body, my arms have always been my pistons. Which did lead to some unexpected problems. I'm not talking about chronic traumatic brain encephalopathy (guess who picked that term), but it could have. Let me explain.

When I was real young and not walking yet, I slept in a crib, like any other. From a kid's perspective, holding onto those bars and looking out at everyone walking around at their free will, it is a goddam prison cell, no matter how many mobiles, stuffed animals, pillows, and rattles are there. Fortunately, it doesn't have a roof, so escape is merely a few arm pulls away. I tried many times to pull my puny body over the top of the crib to reach freedom, but it took about 3 months for me to get the necessary strength. Then, in the middle of no particularly special night, I woke up around 3 am and looked over to where my parents were sleeping in this huge bed with lots of pillows and fluffy blankets and it just set me off. Fine, they let me sleep in their room, but in a private cell? Sure, it was mahogany and nicely appointed, but it wasn't a bed. Something snapped in my head and there must have been a surge in my adrenaline, because suddenly, I pulled myself up to the very top of the crib bars and briefly teetered on the top rim that went all around the crib bars. Looking down, I became aware of a minor miscalculation–it was a long way down to the floor. I went for it, flipped over and landed with a thump on the carpeted floor. I'll be honest. I don't know if I knocked myself out or simply fell back asleep, but somehow I rolled all the way back under the crib which was against a wall. And there I slept the rest of the night.

In the morning, I heard my dad walk over to the crib and rummage around all the crap in it. He called over to my mother, "Where'd Shane go?" She sleepily replied, "He's in the crib." He responded, "No, he's fucking not!" And the search was on. I thought about coming out, but decided to let this play itself out. My dad tore through the apartment, searching every closet, under all the furniture (skipping the most obvious place, the fool), throwing kitchen pots and pans all over the place. My mother was completely frantic and yelling "where could he have gone!" and doing her own separate search. I think my mom started crying and my dad was calming her down, saying, "He has to be here somewhere, the doors and windows are all locked–it's not like he was abducted." This was way before all the kids on milk cartons. I decided after a few minutes to come out, fearing the worst, but I learned one of the most important lessons of my life that morning. I figured they would scream at me and put a fucking roof over the crib top and leave me there in solitary for a week. But here's what happened. I poked my head out just a bit for my dad to see and he yelled, 'There he is, under the crib." They scooped me up with such joy and relief that I felt like a prince. Then my dad clinically looked me over and found a small bump on my forehead and exclaimed, "Shit, he somehow made it over the top of the crib and fell on the floor. Got a bruise on his forehead. Seems OK, otherwise. How the hell did he get out of there? He can't even stand up on his own." The fool underestimated my bulging arms and pulling myself up by the bars.

Well, they were so relieved and thankful that I was OK, that they decided their only recourse was guilt. My mother said, "He really could have gotten hurt, that's like a 5 foot fall." And my dad concurred. So they decided it was too risky to attempt to imprison me again. The crib mattress was placed on the floor, surrounded by a wall of pillows, on all four sides. Nowhere to fall and a newfound sense of freedom, but still not in the holy grail of the Big Bed they were sleeping in. The very next night, I awoke around the same time and I undertook the brutal task of breaking through the pillow wall, pulling myself along the floor with just my arms (I never learned to crawl properly–ever–don't ask) and reaching their bed, which fortunately was on a box spring on the floor, nice and low. I quietly climbed up and insinuated myself between the two of them, without so much as a peep; they didn't even move. And I fell asleep free at last.

In the morning, they awoke with me in the middle. My dad cracked up and my mom dreamily awakened with laughter as well. She asked, "Why did you put him in bed with us? I thought we decided that was a bad idea and habit forming." He answered, "I thought you put him in here. You didn't?" They laughed some more, then I laughed (they fucking woke me up), and we all cuddled and tickled and did all that Disney family movie shit stuff that seemed cool at the time, and it really was. Nevertheless, next night I was back on the crib mattress with more pillows around it then ever. But screw that, I made it back to what I later termed "the little middle"–a line that became a lifelong family joke I might add–the very next night and for two nights thereafter. Finally, they saw the light and the fruitlessness of infant incarceration, and I became a co-habitant of the Big Bed for several more years, until I got too big.

So what did I learn? I learned that when you do something that might get you in trouble, make it seem like you did even worse. Then when the truth comes out and it's not as bad as it seems, nothing happens. You get away with it. If you can throw in a minor injury, all the better. My dad told me a story when I was much older about this over beers, his beer and my root beer, I don't drink very much. He said that when he was in high school and was going to come home later than his parental curfew, he would call his mother and tell her he would be late, that he had been picked up by the police and was in jail. His mother would yell and scream for about 15 seconds, and then he would say, "I'm only kidding. We're just running a little late and I'll be home in an hour. I just didn't want you to worry." And sure enough, his mother was so relieved he wasn't in jail, that when he came home, he got a big kiss and went to bed with nary a word about 2 hours of tardiness.

Moral: When you do something bad, make sure it looks worse than it is, throw in a little risk of personal harm, and when things settle out, you'll be the better for it. I've used this on more than a few occasions.

Chapter 3
The Crab Stampede

The whole puny leg thing was both a curse and a bless-ing. The curse is obvious. If the wheels can't get you around sufficiently, your world obviously becomes a lot smaller and freedom becomes fleeting, at the mercy of fatigue. On the other hand, if you are an unreliable walker and can evoke the pity that is self-evident in my situation and you go places with family and friends that require walking, you actually get people to CARRY YOU everywhere. I'm talking riding shoulders for miles on end, seeing the whole world two steps ahead of everyone you are with. Imagine that. Think about it for a minute. You're tired or sore or just don't feel like walking. Imagine turning to the person next to you, extending your arms without a word, but widening your big baby blues, and boom, they automatically pick you up. Yeah, yeah, I know, all little kids do this crap, but I got to do it for maybe 6 or 7 years! And towards the end of that time, it took development of several intricate strategies to prolong it as much as I could, as well as alternative strategies to terminate unwanted trips even when I was being carried.

In general, short trips were of no consequence. If the carrier was going up to the store on a quick errand, who cares having a featherweight on their shoulders. It's good for a laugh, it's even fun for the two. But longer treks were more problematic. I knew of my leg fatigue, but it took awhile to comprehend that the carrier not only had leg fatigue, but back pain and shoulder strain commensurate with the length of the journey. I may have been small for my age, but I was still a sack of taters. How was a little guy like me supposed to know? Admittedly, I was selfish, egocentric, thoughtless, arrogant, petulant, and self-serving. On careful re-consideration, though, I wouldn't change a thing. Every man for himself. I think it helped keep my dad in better shape.

My first vague recollection of the brutality of my strategy occurred when we went camping at John Pennekamp Coral Reef State Park in the Florida Keys in the latter 1970's. We did a lot of beach walking, with me riding high on my dad's shoulders. I was unaware that walking in sand is particularly tiring, but that wasn't my problem. It soon began to take a toll on my father after a couple of days, and one fine afternoon he started getting bad leg cramps, something I have never had the pleasure of experiencing, since I believe I have never walked a long enough distance for that to occur. In any event, they got bad enough that I began to ride my mom's shoulders for a while. They had miscalculated and we were too far down the beach; then she soon began to suffer as well. They bizarrely came to the conclusion that I needed to walk. Think about it–the sand was killing them and they wanted the little handicapper to walk on his own. No way that was going to happen. They put me down, stood me up, each grabbed one of my hands and started walking. I took a couple of steps and realized several things. First, the sand was fucking hot. And it was impossible to walk in it. And worst of all, I was setting an unacceptable precedent. So I did the only thing I could think of–I went limp. Not leg limp. I allowed every muscle in my body to relax and collapsed in a heap at their feet. First, they gently scolded me, then they encouraged me, then they pathetically begged and pleaded with me to get up and walk. But principles are sacred things, and I never wanted them to think I would just walk at their mere request. So I remained completely and totally limp: legs, arms, back, shoulders, everything. Grab my hand and I swung like a hanging bag of laundry. Let my head flop backwards too, as a special effect. They looked crushed and I knew then that I had an incredible tool for controlling my environment that would last for years. It took them a few hours to make it back to the campsite and they were not very pleased, but I incurred no significant wrath. I think they were simply disappointed. Well, I have had lots of disappointments too, and it was a good lesson for them. Don't carry me anywhere, if you can't carry me back as well.

When we finally made it back to the campsite, everyone was pretty tuckered out and quiet. And they were sore, in both senses of the word. But dinner was fixed, spirits brightened a bit, and everyone was looking forward to crabbing at midnight albeit with painful legs. This is how you do it: You get a smelly fish head and tie it to a strong string and then drop it off the edge of the pier. You watch it with a flashlight since it's not that deep and you can see the bluepoint crabs slowly crawling on to the head, having their late dinner. You slowly bring the head back up without disturbing the crabs and when it nears the surface, you grab a net on a long pole and scoop those babies up. Boom, before you know it, you got buckets of crabs on ice for a supposedly fine meal. Let me state unequivocally, that I found the whole thing disgusting, the crabs terrifying, and I wouldn't eat one of those things for all the money in the world, even with a ton of ketchup, which generally makes everything tolerable to eat. Furthermore, it turns out that my parents hadn't a clue as to what they were doing. Someone had told them this was the way to do it, and they simply followed the directions. Admittedly it seemed to work, at least for a while. But I knew something wasn't quite right when my mom asked my dad, "Are they dead when you take them out of the water and put them on ice?" My dad pretentiously responded, "Of course they're dead. Look at them. You see any of them moving? We have a lot of crabs here and should give some to other campers. We'll have a feast for dinner tomorrow." Totally clueless, cause I saw one of them claws move, for sure. But my dad's legs were still sore, he was a bit cranky, and he put those iced crab buckets just outside the tent and we all went to sleep around 4 am..

Around 6 am, I awoke in the tent that just so happened to be unzipped in front, surrounded by 4 of the most vicious, mean, vile, and pissed off crabs you ever saw. They were hissing at me!! I started screaming, which quickly awakened my parents who chuckled at the sight, until one of them latched on to my mom's hand and pinched her good, gaining a nice little yelp. Suddenly, there were more screams and yelling, kids and adults alike. Seems all the crabs woke up as the ice melted and they made a break for it. We're talking 60 or more crabs on a wild rampage tearing through everything in their path. It was a crab stampede!! I swear, the four in my tent were hissing at me and staring me down. I screamed louder and my dad chased them into a corner, and grabbed each to toss them out the front of the tent. Appropriately, he got pinched a couple of times as well. I went without a scratch, as it should be. But it soon became apparent that the entire campsite was now awake and being invaded by scores of vicious crabs, intent on either making it back to the water or inflicting as much pain as possible on all the folks trying to round them up. I didn't witness much after that, since there was no way I was going outside, but suffice to say the massacre went on for 15 or 20 minutes.

Probably 20 or so crabs made their escape, a bunch of kids got nipped and were crying, parents were either laughing or more likely getting pissed off about their kids and getting awakened, and my parents were nervously evaluating the situation to determine if we should either give away all the remaining crabs or just make a run for it. We ended up staying and no one sued us. We shared crabs with anyone who wanted them, which seemed to mollify most people.

This is what camping with my parents is like.

Chapter 4
My Cuban Heritage

Perhaps my best memories of those early days were at the underground Cuban beauty salon where I spent a considerable amount of time when my parents were at work. It became my daycare center and my name changed to Shanito ('Little Shane' in Spanish), as determined by the many patrons. I never knew it until I was older, but back then most of the few daycare centers in existence (they were just starting up then) wouldn't take people like me because of my 'special needs'–in those days they didn't say special needs, though. I was simply retarded. Too much work, too much liability (not my choice of word). I asked my dad about it later in life and he said it was a pile of shit. I had no special needs for a fucking daycare center. I ate and drank when I was told to, I took my scheduled naps, likely more so than other kids since I love to sleep and still nap every day, I played without injuring the other kids, and I was so damn happy all day long with a really upbeat demeanor that put those other kids to shame. But alas, no one would take me except one place in the Little Havana section of Miami. I went there a couple of weeks and the people were really nice, though one seeming downside was that nobody spoke English. Then one day my mom got stuck at work and called and asked if she could pick me up an hour late. They said no, but one of the girls working there, Mary (who would soon become one of my 'sisters') said she would take me to her parents' house nearby and my mom could pick me up there. So that was the plan. I went home with her and when the front door opened, there was the most beautiful smiling woman's face I have ever seen, looking at me dressed in some crappy little coordinated sailor outfit (or it could have been my cool Superman outfit, but I can't remember). She gently took me from her daughter and that was that. We fell in love instantly. She said I was a gift from God, and I felt the same way about her, though I really don't have a clue as to what God's gifts are like. Sometimes these things just happen. She sat on the couch holding me, hugging me, laughing, and kissing my forehead and saying how beautiful I was (which was/is a truthful statement) and we both just melted in mutual warmth. It felt great. By the time my mom got there, the plan had been hatched. Elena (that's her name–but I still call her 'Meh' to this day, to distinguish her from my 'mom') simply said that I wasn't going back to the daycare anymore, that I was going to spend my days with her caring for me at the beauty parlor she ran in her house. Now this seemed pretty straightforward to me, but my mom was a bit nervous. They talked awhile and then my parents discussed it and given their complete lack of adulthood and parental competence, they agreed to it, since it was primarily the daughter who was watching me at the daycare center anyway. And since they didn't speak Spanish, they really didn't have a clue as to what was going on at either place, in terms of mass murderers, child abuse, starvation, beatings, etc. Yup, these are my parents. They couldn't communicate with the people at the daycare center, they couldn't communicate with Elena and only just a bit with her husband, Hector (one really cool dude, but who had a day job and knew little of the goings on at the beauty parlor), and they couldn't communicate with me really, since I couldn't talk yet and mostly explained myself with hand gestures, emotions, countenance, and general lack of scarring from physical abuse. But I was generally cleaner when I came home than when my mom brought me in. So fortunately, their gross parental incompetence allowed me the chance of a lifetime to obtain the most loving unrelated 'second mother' one could ever hope to find. A real life changer. I became a member of their family, and so did my parents to a slightly lesser extent.

Now day-to-day life in an underground Cuban beauty parlor hidden in someone's home may seem an unusual setting for day care, especially when you are the only kid there, and a gringo handicapper to boot, but you would be sorely mistaken. Not only did Elena love me, all the patrons loved me as well, just not as much as her. At first, everyone fought over holding me, feeding me, changing me, pampering me. I am told there was one lady who was standoffish about me, which immediately prompted Elena to terminate her as a client. My days were fabulous. I got cool clothing, gifts, toys, multiple baths, naps, more playtime than I ever got at daycare or home for that matter. I had my hair done EVERYDAY. And not just hair. I was like an experimental doll for everyone to work on. I had curlers put in my hair, had manicures, nails polished, makeup placed, lipstick–you name it, I had it done to me. Why? Because I loved being the center of attention and they all loved playing with me.

Some of the clothing stuff was pretty weird, too. I mean, my parents weren't exactly 'fashionistas', but I sorta liked all the cartoon character themed pajamas and little animal figures all over my clothes. I really didn't care that much, though. But Elena and her friends took it to a whole other level. They would bring in this guy who reeked of cigars and took a measuring tape, wrapping it all around me. He was called a tailor for what it's worth. In a week or two he would reappear with things like a red velvet tuxedo, stripes on the pants and collar, with all sorts of frilly additions. Or frilly shirts, weird shorts with matching tops, almost everything in bright red and gold trim. I would look in the mirror, and I gotta say, I thought it was pretty cool at the time–I felt like I was at a wedding or something. And all the women would gush over me even more, which always pleased me. But when my parents saw me, they would smile and tell Elena, her family and any women within hearing distance how nice I looked. Once we got home though, those clothes disappeared into the bottom of my closet, never to be seen again. And I was cautioned never to try to put them on. Later in life, I realized it was a cultural thing. What was cool for hippie-looking freaks like my dad were not a part of the Cuban fashion culture and vice versa. But the intentions were good, and I still had fun with it. We all go through phases. And frankly, I have learned it's all a matter of taste. I loved bell-bottomed pants way back when, but who would put that crap on again. I am just a jeans and T-shirt guy now, mostly because that's what my parents are. If it was up to me, I would wear tasteful suits, collared shirts and a tie. I would look very distinguished all the time. But the tyranny of my parents prevails to this day.

Another reason I let those women do anything they wanted to me was that most of these gorgeous ladies were in various states of undress all day long. At an underground beauty parlor, it's very informal, and woman take off their blouses and skirts and walk around in bras and undies when they get their hair colored or permed and for other stuff as well, though I don't know exactly what the hell they were doing there all the time. They would usually clean me up before my mom came to get me, but once in awhile I still had lipstick or curlers on, and my mom would just smile and shake her head while Elena cleaned me up for the outside world.

But for me, it was my introduction to the females of our species, and I believe it made me the sexist that I am today. There is absolutely no question in my mind that women are far superior to men in virtually everything and I would rather hang with women than guys anytime and every time, except maybe during ballgames and wrestling matches.

Over time, I got passed along to other family members and close friends who took me to parks, petting zoos, lunches, tricycle rides–you name it, I did it. I sipped Cuban coffee with old guys playing dominoes in the parks, beers in backyard beer gardens. I used to go to the park with really nice women, one of whose husband would sometimes come by and play catch with me and try to teach me to throw and catch. Well, I never did learn to catch very well, but I could throw the ball a mile and I'm pretty sure he had a big part of it. Turns out that a few years later when we moved to Minnesota, my mom got a call from that lady, who said they had moved to Minneapolis as well and she wanted to see me. My mom didn't know her by name but called Elena on the phone, who verified her as one of my many Cuban lady friends. So my dad calls to set up a get together in a park one weekend. When he asked what they were doing in Minneapolis, she said her husband was working for the Minnesota Twins baseball team as a coach. My dad looked down at the paper with her name on it and saw Mrs. Pascual and his eyes bugged out. Little did I know that the guy who taught me to throw was Camilo Pascual, a famous major league baseball pitcher (5 time All-Star). Not only did I not know that, but my parents didn't even know that I ever went to any park or that anyone was teaching me to throw a ball. My father thought he had taught me to throw. I'll give him a little credit, because he had a pretty good amateur arm, but forget being mentioned in the same breath as Camilo, who was just a great guy and is most responsible for my solid throwing arm—which I might add helped me to an athlete-of-the-year award later in life.

The main things that go on in an underground Cuban beauty parlor are the usual hair, skin, hand and nails things, but there is a whole other world of gossip (in Spanish, of course), screaming, yelling, laughing and crying—all in good fun—lots of pastries (pastelitos), Cuban coffee, homemade dishes brought in by the customers (who are mostly friends anyway), tons of desserts, and more affection than anyone could ever imagine. My emotional stability and well-being were clearly established in that place and have lasted a lifetime. I was a part of everything. Everything brought to eat passed into my mouth and to this day I love malanga (sort of a mashed potato dish) with raw egg on top of it, as much as anything, but my parents hate it and won't use raw eggs, so it's a distant memory now. But I became the centerpiece of the parlor for years. Sometimes, they wouldn't even give me back to my parents for a weekend because they wanted to take me somewhere like Disney World. My parents would simply ask if I wanted to stay, and I invariably said yes, since who wants to spend every weekend with their parents. Frankly, who wants to spend any weekend with their parents—only kidding.

And I was so spoiled, it was tremendous. No matter what I did, I could do no wrong. I even inadvertently helped Elena out with a big problem she had with her interior decorating. Seems Hector had brought home this large statue of a red bull and placed it on the center coffee table of the living room. To him, it was a majestic piece of art. Even I knew it was a Velvet Elvis—I know this term now because my mom is an artist but it was just understood then. I think he got it in Mexico, which I know about since I now live near Mexico, in Arizona. Anyway, Hector loved this bull

statue, but Elena and her daughters (that's Mary and Evelyn) hated it and thought it was the ugliest thing this side
of Fort Lauderdale. One day I was on the floor right next to
the coffee table and reached up and pushed the bull about
two inches toward the edge. As a man of conscience and
concern for my own well-being, I glanced at Elena to look
for a reaction and found none. And she was watching and
smiling. So I pushed it another couple of inches towards
the edge. She smiled and said nothing. Then I got brave
and pushed it so one front leg was off the table completely.
Elena was beaming and happily rattled off something in
Spanish, that I understood a little–meaning that she didn't
give a rat's ass about that bull. That was good enough for
me. I gave it a good shove, off it went, shattering into a
million pieces on the hard tile floor. Elena smiled and said,
"Oh my goodness" in her heavy Spanish accent and quickly
snatched me away so as not to get scratched by shards. She
cleaned it up, smiling the whole time and nary a word of
annoyance was uttered. When Hector got home, nothing
was said during dinner (I was staying over that night).
When everyone went into the living room to watch TV, he
said something in Spanish and pointed to the former rest-
ing place of the bull. Elena said something and smiled at
me. Hector shook his head and mumbled something else.
Elena got pissed and snapped something back at Hector,
who abruptly changed course, came over and scooped me
up with a smile, and said in his pretty good English, "It's
OK, Shanito, I'm glad you didn't get hurt. I know where I
can get another one. You are a good man." Elena, Evelyn,
and Mary took on horrified looks and one of his daughters
said, "Dad, the bull obviously scared him. We think that's
why he pushed it away." Which was the biggest shit-faced
lie I had heard to that date. Hector paused a moment and
looked at me, smiling my best grin right into his eye sock-
ets, and he said something else in Spanish which seemed

to relieve everyone in the room, except him. Yeah, I know I got used, but who cares. I got to smash a statue and made almost an entire family happy.

But you gotta understand something. I wasn't LIKE family. I BECAME family. I WAS family. I mean you don't meet a lot of people like this everyday. Forget about the special bond between me and Elena. Hector was just a great guy to be around and like a 'second father'. I would sometimes go to watch him play baseball in serious baseball league games around Miami, and he was the dude. The man could play ball. And he showed me sometimes how he could cook better than Elena and we would have special lunches together. We ate like pigs and it was great food, but I never told him he was out of his class in the kitchen compared to his wife. But we cruised around a lot in Little Havana and I tell you, Hector knew every person in every section of the whole place. It was very cool. Parks, cafes, restaurants, and all sorts of hangouts became a new part of my world.

And Mary and Evelyn simply became my sisters. They helped take care of me, played with me, took me with them when they went to sees friends, took me to movies, baby sat me, and overall were just perfect sisters.

I know. It sounds fake. That I'm making this up. But you'd be wrong. And my dad has always said no family is perfect–you get what you are born into. But see, I found the loophole. I got to 'pick' my second family, from a chance encounter. Pure serendipity (great looking word and I approved it, though I couldn't learn to pronounce it in 20 years). But someone needs to give me some credit for the perfect pick. It was my enthusiasm that hooked us all up, though their enthusiasm wasn't far behind. And let me finally say, no, they aren't really 'perfect' because no one is, but they sure were great lottery picks.

Chapter 5
My first gigs as an actor and working in a hospital

Sadly, I am a former, washed up, child actor. You know, those cute kids who are on TV for awhile with no particular talent, but good looks and charisma. They wake up one day at age 15 and they are washed up. Gone. Forgotten. Headed for a life of drug addiction, alcoholism, crime, divorces, tabloids that dig them up in flophouses, weighing 400 pounds with prostitutes only slightly slimmer (this is my dad's description). Fortunately, I didn't come to this endpoint. This is mostly because I was a character actor of sorts. I got bit roles here and there and because they NEVER PAID ME, I never got the big head. Or the babes. I was able to keep my perspective on the humility of the human condition.

In reality, I never had a spoken word, which is good, since no one would have understood it. And the few parts were commercials or news shows (human interest segments), for non-profit organizations, which doesn't lend itself easily to fame or fortune. For which I am grateful, for who wants to end up weighing 400 pounds with a drug problem and a bunch of fat prostitutes.

My TV premiere was on a Florida United Way commercial starring me, with Perry Como as my sidekick, that was on TV every night, multiple times for a couple of months. On the commercial he's holding me and he was a pretty cool guy at the shoot. Very mellow. Sleepy mellow. They say his music was like that too, but I wouldn't know. I even got an action scene coming down a playground slide. And I was only about 2 or 3 years old then. I got about 30 seconds of face time on a one minute commercial, but now that I have the video of it, I know I was a pure amateur. I just didn't understand what they were doing and blew my shot at humor, posing, or just hamming it up. How was I supposed to know? I changed that in later performances.

The first time it came on TV in our house, my parents stood up in disbelief. They were truly shocked and asked me what it was all about. Given my pathetic communication skills, I couldn't lay it out for them so they had to call around and found out that I was picked because my blue eyes were bigger than my head, I had blonde Beatle-cut hair (thanks to Elena), I was mellow for a long shoot, and frankly, I was the best looking handicapped kid they could find. Never really found out who picked me. Of course, my deeply involved parents were completely unaware they had signed all the forms I brought home from someplace or other, allowing me to be on the commercial. I can always count on them to watch out for my benefit. Well, the first few nights, whenever the commercial came on, they jumped up and were thrilled. After a few days, it began to get pretty repetitious and finally the "Thrill is Gone" came to pass (I love BB King, the blues, and any music you can dance to–and to this day I can dance with the best of them). We all stopped watching it and were greatly relieved when it finally disappeared. In those days, you couldn't record anything from your TV (my god, I would be missing all my current wrestling pay per views, basketball games, TV shows–how archaic), so it could have disappeared forever, as an unsubstantiated claim. But this really cool guy who was the Director of the hospital my mom worked at, got a reel of the film recording from the United Way when he heard about it, and over the years, it has been transferred to VHS and then DVD. I guess you are wondering why he would do that. Well, because he was a good guy. You see, sometimes when there was an emergency or something that I couldn't understand, I couldn't go to Elena's and my mom would take me to her office where she worked with lots of numbers. In those days, people didn't do that, but my mom did. She didn't really give a shit what anyone said and only a few people made any negative comments. Most folks loved me because as I have told you before, I am a very lovable guy. This Director guy came by one day and HE took a liking to me and started having me come by his office sometimes to hang with him. He even brought toys into his office for me to play with. He had a TV IN HIS OFFICE!!! I'm telling you, there are a lot of great people in this world. Another of my mom's bosses lived right near our apartment and she was like another family member–I hung out in her apartment all the time playing with her two dogs and when my mom was busy at work and I had to go in with her, I sometimes hung out with Genie (that's her name) in her office. She has been my friend for life, even though we live very far apart.

Genie's mom was a really cool lady, too. I used to sit with her at night and we would watch reruns of The Lawrence Welk Show. For those of you who don't know the musical traditions of American TV, it was an incredibly lame show of orchestras and singers and dancers, that likely was created for handicapped people who have no ear for music. But I loved it as I loved many horribly out-of-fashion things as a child. I think everyone does that until at some point in your life, a light bulb goes off, and you realize you're an idiot. My mom and Genie had already seen the light bulb, and would just laugh and go outside on the patio so as not to see or even hear that show. But me and Genie's mom, we were completely into it and I make no apology. Everyone goes through phases. Though this one was a bit embarrassing.

Anyway, once the word got out that I was a buddy with the big shots, no one could say anything about me being at my mom's work. That's how things work. You oughtta know that.

Chapter 6
Boxing and catching the damn ball

I've already told you I had good upper body strength. And I must admit, part of that was my dad working out with me a lot in all sorts of games involving balls, moving myself around with my arms since I still couldn't walk, and especially boxing. When he came home from work at the hospital, the first thing he did after picking me up and tossing me around like a pillow, was to lie on the floor with me sitting on his belly and we would box. He would only tap me with his fingers but I made big fists and hauled off on him. I never could figure out why I couldn't nail him in the face–I always went for the face. He would just laugh and knock my hands away. But he let me pound as hard as I wanted on his chest and belly and it made him laugh even harder. My mom would watch from the kitchen and smile her beneficent smile and in short order, she took me to the toy store and we picked out the coolest bright red boxing gloves I've ever seen. That night we whipped them out for my dad to see, who was beaming when he saw them. I got laced up and we went to it. It made a great sound when I hit his chest and I banged on it till my arms were sore. Then suddenly, my mom yelled something to my dad from the kitchen and he turned his head for an instant, and I saw the opening immediately. Two quick shots to his mouth when he wasn't looking and then some blood dripping down his chin. I didn't knock him out, he didn't cry, and he never stopped smiling. But the man got two stitches for a split lip and as far as I am concerned, it was a TKO.

Tit for tat, my dad tormented me with trying to catch a ball, resulting in some of my own blood being spilled. He had this thing about improving my 'coordination', which I think meant catching the fucking ball. I still don't get how everyone catches balls so easily. I am a sports fanatic–I've practiced with the Philadelphia 76'ers, the Temple University basketball team, some Philadelphia Phillies and all sorts of star athletes and let me say that the most incredible thing to me is that they always catch the damn ball. Forget the shots (I can do that now), forget the dunks (I cannot do that now except in Nerf basketball), forget all the other athletic stuff. How the hell do they always catch the ball and never take it in the face?

We started with big soft balls that we rolled back and forth on the floor while seated. Pretty easy. I got over-confident. Then we stood up (I got propped up against furniture) and bounced it to each other–a whole other story. I kept ducking or flopping out of the way cause after a few shots to the face, it was clear I was going to get it in the face endlessly. He got us real close together so he was practically catching it for me and that worked for me. But over time he kept trying to teach me to catch the ball, any ball, from a direct air toss. We used those soft pink rubber balls, tennis balls, kick balls, under-inflated beach balls, you name it. I couldn't do it. Every time I would eventually get it in the face and it really pissed me off when my dad would chuckle. Oh, he tried to hide it, but I knew he was getting a kick out of my misery. I would get real pissed off, and given my good arm, would always throw it as hard as I could at his face, but somehow, he always caught it. I've gotten better and I'm sort of OK with a basketball (I can shoot great). But throw me a baseball and I'm still going to close my eyes, turn my head and make sure I am so far away from that ball that there is not a chance it will touch me. Am I embarrassed by it? Yeah, a little. Especially around small kids who somehow have acquired the skill. Such is life–everyone has their limitations. You have to expose yourself fully in a memoir or so I am told.

Chapter 7
Shrimping, scamming, and kissing

All in all, my formative Miami years were simply a pleasure. It may have been only my first 4 years of life, but the memories are really ingrained in me. A lot of people say they can't remember stuff that early, but I remember everything–I almost have a photographic memory. I remember making my parents ride "It's a Small World" at Disney World over and over (occasionally alternating with "Mr. Toad's Wild Ride") for hours on end and I happen to know they didn't like it very much. I appreciate that selflessness, but again, that was their job. One time the ride broke and we were stopped in the same place for an hour, but the music kept playing. I think it's a pretty good–not great–song they play down there. I danced the whole time we were stuck. My parents seemed to get more and more annoyed. Well, maybe annoyed isn't the right word. I think they actually started to look sickened. And, to this day, if either of them hears that song, their faces go white, and they scramble to get away from the sound or turn it off, if it's coming from some place they can control. They do seem to get ill from it. Weird. Sometimes I sing it to them just to annoy them, if they piss me off. Disney World was a great place, though I think I have outgrown it now. It ain't Vegas, though even Vegas is starting to lose its edge. We can talk about that later.

To sum it up, Miami was the place I became a little man. I came to know I was different from a lot of people, but in a way that most people were nicer to me than to the 'normal' kids. Oh, I got my share of stares as I have most of my life, but I played my heart out, learned to eat great Cuban food, got a second family who loved me almost as much as my mom and dad, and cruised all over the place. We went fishing in the Everglades (don't park your boat near the mangroves–the mosquitoes are brutal), went to all sorts of concerts, sporting events, and lots of cheap restaurants that still had great food (my parents didn't have much money then). Italian has always been my favorite. But the best was going to the beaches. Not Miami Beach, which was OK, but the beaches of Key Biscayne, which were the best. We used to hang out on the beach at the Hotel Sonesta there and use the pools, get free towels, drink at the beach bar and get snacks, and mingle with tons of people. We went so often on weekends that we even got known there by the employees, which made it even better, cause they treated us even more special. Which is really pretty funny because we couldn't afford anything there except the drinks. Turns out, as my dad later told me, that the dingy little room where we were staying on the beach actually wasn't part of the luxurious Hotel Sonesta. It was called the Silver Sands Motel and was right next door. $19.95 a night. We would sleep there (don't blame me, I didn't know from nothin') and every morning simply stroll along the beach over to the ritzy place to spend the days and evenings, except when we needed to shower or change clothes. See, back then, my dad was a bit of a scam artist and said he wanted the best for us and if this was how it had to be done, so be it. He didn't like rich people then, and doesn't much now, though he became a doctor and we ended up being upper middle class, a word that has no meaning to me and was written into the story by him. Another of his literary intrusions. But if it had to be done, I guess I'm OK with it, cause I guess I like the rich life too. Hypocrisy at its finest.

Key Biscayne in those days still had lots of shrimp and we sometimes would go out in a small, borrowed little row-boat at night with a flashlight and look for them in the water. It's real easy to go shrimping like that. Towards the end of our stay in Miami, even I was able to scoop up bunches of them with a smaller net. I'm not saying I'm Forrest Gump (one of my favorite movies), but I am a veteran crabber, fisherman, and shrimper going back to these early years. I wouldn't eat any of those disgusting things, but why would you when you got great homemade Cuban food (Elena taught my mom to be a great Cuban cook). Fortunately, no one told me at the time that I was eating some of those disgusting creatures IN the Cuban food, but what the hell. They were well disguised in the rice.

There was a small public beach along the bay near one of our favorite bars (I think it was the Rusty Nail or some slick name like that) that had these incredible deformed trees that you could climb. Well, I couldn't climb them, but my parents were young and frisky then, and they would climb this one special tree with me sitting by the trunk on the ground. We always did this at sunset and early evening and sometimes had a picnic. It was hard to see at night, but I know for sure that when they got up in that tree with my mom snuggling with my dad, they were doing the kissing thing, you know, the one where you put your tongue in the other person's mouth. They seemed pretty happy about it and clearly thought I was out of view. Over the years I've tried it quite a few times myself. Most of the time the girls get pissed off, but every once in awhile...........

The Minneapolis Years–or maybe just a year and a half

Chapter 1
No Cubans, some Indians, and stupid little kids

I wish I could tell you more about the Florida years, because I think they were better than I can even remember. But I do remember being just so happy all the time. But let's face it, how much can you remember from years 0–4, even with the help of your parents. I mean most of the time they were at work and missed my entire daily scene and had to learn about it by word of mouth. Not their fault or anything like that, but there wasn't a lot going on from 0–2 that I can recollect. I wasn't a musical prodigy playing the piano at 3 years of age–I was 'retarded'. OK, it's time to move on to the politically correct terms that even I prefer now as compared to the insults–though I still have a mildly favorable view of 'Mongol', as discussed above. So I was 'developmentally disabled' or 'handicapped'. Unfortunately I cannot pronounce even these words sufficiently to use them in conversation, so I generally avoid the whole topic and when someone points out some limitation of mine, I simply say 'I can't do that' with perfect clarity. Then they leave me alone.

Talk about culture and weather shock when we moved

to Minneapolis! The only Spanish-speaking people I met when I was there were Mr. and Mrs. Pascual. There were almost no black people. I say black because that was the most acceptable term at the end of the 1970's, though now I am told that African-American is the preferred word. I haven't a clue why that changed, but I prefer the term 'black'. This is because for most of my life I have always considered myself to be black. This is despite my blonde hair, blue eyes, and extremely white skin. I just always liked black people best, which in Miami was a combination of black Cubans and black African-Americans. I think it's because they are culturally more outgoing than white people and seem to have more fun—at least with me, though I certainly don't discriminate against white people. Some of my very best friends are white. As you read on, there were a few years when I thought I was Asian, while we lived in San Francisco, but we'll deal with that later.

One of the first things I noticed when we moved to Minneapolis was that, in addition to no blacks or Hispanics, I never saw other developmentally disabled people either. I'm talking almost NEVER. Where the hell were they hiding? It's not like people were nasty to me—in fact, I made some really good friends during my short stay in Minneapolis. People in restaurants, bars, cafes, movies, sporting events, and almost everywhere, were very nice to me, and I appreciated that. But I couldn't see where they put the handicappers. They just weren't around to be seen. Maybe it was the times in that particular place—I don't know, I am not a sociologist. Maybe they didn't have many developmentally disabled people, but I doubt that. Maybe like me, the disabled didn't want to go outside because it was so fucking cold, but that was only for around 6 months, and after a short adjustment period I did fine just being bundled up and carried almost anywhere.

But there were a fair number of Indians around, and I

really liked Indians, who are now called Native Americans. I saw them mostly in the streets, rather than in restaurants or around the university. Even I knew they were having problems, because a lot of them seemed drunk and were begging for change. And people seemed to treat them like shit, calling them names I had never heard before or since. I've always felt bad about that, even as a little kid, and I would always give them whatever change I had, since it seems that's what some people did. My dad always made me carry 10 dollars in my pocket, which he later told me, was for an emergency, but I have no idea what he was talking about. There's not exactly a lot of cabs driving around the Minneapolis streets when you get separated and lost and I didn't even know my address back then. I didn't even know what a taxi was until we moved to Philadelphia much later. Whatever, it made him feel better, until one day I gave my 10 dollars to a Native American (got that right, didn't I?) and I thought my dad was going to pass out. He yelled at me and said I should never do that and I replied that I saw him give out change all the time. What was the problem? I still don't really get it, but I'm not good with numbers. He said I gave too much money to one guy and that I should spread it around in smaller amounts. I told him that I didn't understand, but he somehow got through to me and I stuck with handing out coins for a long time. Sometimes I gave money to people who weren't even begging and they looked shocked and wanted to give it back. I just told them to keep it and have fun. They thought I was nuts, but I knew money bought good things and it has always made me feel good giving away money, especially since my dad just gives me more. I still piss off my dad to this day when we go to our favorite bar in Tucson and I go alone from the outside patio to get a drink from the bartender inside, unaccompanied. About half the time I tell them to keep the change, just when the spirit moves me. I have noticed that when it's a

$5 bill, my dad reacts calmly, but he gets pretty pissed when I leave a $20 bill behind. So unless he doesn't have smaller bills, I usually get some singles or a fiver. And most of the bartenders end up coming out and giving the extra change back to me, since we are regulars and they are great people, so generally I am protected from screwing things up on the financial end.

Now that I think of it, what's with all the name changing of everyone? Blacks become African-Americans, Cubans become Hispanic, Indians become Native Americans, and Mongoloids become 'developmentally disabled.' No one changed or anything, just the names. Pretty weird, don't you think?

I didn't think about it much at first, but it became quickly apparent that I was getting about 5000 per cent more stares whenever we went out to eat or do stuff. This was not true in the area around our neighborhood, which was called Dinkytown, and the nearby Cedar-Riverside area, which is the University of Minnesota area. People there were totally cool–probably because it was a lot of immature, fun-loving, raucous students who generally didn't give a shit about anything, let alone seeing a handicapper. Sort of like my parents. I believe everyone else in the city had the misfortune of not knowing disabled people since they never saw them around and for some reason, I made a small portion of them uncomfortable.

One of my first memories in that city took place in a shopping mall food court, where my mom and I were having lunch. Or maybe it was some other cheap place to eat. Who can remember such insignificant details? Anyway, we're eating our food, and there's this woman at the next table with two kids staring at me. Not just staring though, a little staring has always been a part of my life, except nowadays, when a good-looking stud like me seems to have become a social fad. More on that later. I mean they couldn't take their eyes off me and their mouths were hanging open, wide enough for me to see the food they were chewing. How disgusting! My parents worked hard making sure I ate with my mouth closed and they worked hard to make sure my tongue didn't hang out when I was just doing nothing. You see, when you have Down syndrome, you are born with a humongous tongue and it's hard to not have it hanging out all the time. I hear nowadays, some Downers even have surgery to make it smaller. Gross!!! I've had a few surgeries in my life and I kinda like the whole general anesthesia thing and the pretty nurses, but cutting off a piece of your tongue? No way, Jose. My parents later told me that some speech pathologist (yup, no clue what that is) said to flick my tongue with their finger every time they saw it hanging out and it would hurt just a tad, but just enough to make me put it back inside my mouth. I remember none of this at all, but since I don't have my tongue hanging out at all, I am pleased to hear of this solution, for whatever it's worth. Presumably I must have had a sore tongue for a while but my mom says I didn't cry or anything and that it really wasn't painful, just annoying to me–enough to make me keep it in my mouth. Since my parents have been annoying to me so many times during my life, this seems like a small price to pay for an enhanced social appearance. I'll take their word for it, but who knows?

Where was I–oh yeah, the two kids staring at me. So these two assholes just won't turn their heads away from me. And then, they finally turn to their mother and real loud so I can plainly hear, say, "Mommy, what's wrong with that boy?" And that little slut of a mother answers, "Oh, he's just a retard." And they turn back to staring at me and their mom just looks out into space with empty eyes (I coined that term by the way–my mom uses the word dead eyes). Well, that was it for me. I am a man and was a boy brimming with overconfidence as a direct result of my upbringing by my parents and my choice of friends in Miami. I simply and in my best understandable English, which was adequate for the sentence, said, "What the fuck are you looking at, assholes?" Pretty good for a 5 year old or so with a bad speech impediment.

Well, they sort of freaked and yelled to their mom who heard me quite clearly as well. I emphasized my point by giving them all the finger, which I learned in multiple creative ways from my domino friends in the parks of Little Havana back in Miami–those guys taught me a lot of good stuff. You can give it straight up, sideways, partly covered by the other hand as if you're hiding it from everyone else– all sorts of coolness. The mother's face posed an incredible insult and she said directly to my mother, "Your child is very vulgar, I can tell how he was raised." And she raised her little snout up in the air.

Well, as I've said before, my mom is a gentle soul, but there is one thing in life you can't do and that's cross the line and do anything bad to me, especially calling me names. I don't even know what vulgar means today, but I sure as hell knew they were making fun of me.

So the next thing my mom does is say, "Your children and you are very rude people. We are not rude people." And then raising her voice to be sure the kids heard her quite clearly, she added, "We have been very civil here to specifically NOT stare at your children, because that would be very inappropriate. You should think about that and perhaps you would have more consideration for others."

Then the woman, who was not the brightest of bulbs, took on this dumbshit expression and asked, "What are you talking about? Why would you ever stare at my children?"

"Because your children are the fucking ugliest children we have ever seen. Their faces are deformed, they are incredibly stupid, and they eat like pigs. Clearly a matter of genetics and upbringing." The exact wording is according to my mother–I didn't know what the hell she said except that those people were mighty pissed off.

In retrospect, I didn't notice any of those things, except that they were slob eaters. But pretty quick the two kids starting crying, the mother started panicking, and then started yelling at my mother. "I'm going to call the police! You can't talk to me like that."

"Well, I just did. Go call the police and we will see if they want to arrest us for calling your kids ugly or arrest you for calling my son a retard. I'm sure it would be a fascinating legal case for a judge to hear."

Apparently, this comment sufficed to make the woman grab her two kids and whisk them off in a huff. My mother as always, never yelled or lost her composure, but she sure was smiling for a good ten minutes while I finished my milkshake. I was just glad those jerks were gone.

Chapter 2
Fishing after your bait dies

So we arrived in the summer, and it was a fine time. Lots of cool lakes, beautiful city, and plenty of places to cruise. Good swimming opportunities, though not at the Florida level. One weekend we drove to nearby Wisconsin and went canoeing on a lake and I got my own brand new fishing pole. My dad made a big deal about the whole thing, wrapping it up and giving it to me as a special present the week before we went, just to try to juice me up for the trip. It worked since I became pretty excited at the prospect of going to the beach again. I was sadly disappointed when I found out that rivers and lakes are not even remotely like the ocean beach. The water sort of just sits there and there is no sound of waves, not much in the way of seagulls (my favorite bird in those days), and worst of all, you can almost never see the bottom. I found the whole thing looking rather dirty. Even the smells were wrong. But I kept myself together and braved on.

The whole canoe thing is a mystery to me. I had been in lots of boats before and it made no sense to have a boat in which standing up placed you and everyone in the boat in 'grave peril' of falling in the water. I mean what's the point of that? And it had no motor, so my parents had to paddle all the time with me stuffed on the floor between them suffocating by the oversized bright orange life jacket I was forced to wear. They weren't wearing life jackets, and I was a real good swimmer, so I didn't see the point. Plus, because they were so busy paddling, they hardly talked to me for a long while. Finally, we got to wherever they wanted to be and stopped paddling and, thank god, the fishing lines began to get readied by my dad. My mom loved to GO fishing, but had absolutely no interest in the ACT of fishing at all. She just loved being in the water and was the one who jumped in the most for quick swims. She loved to sunbathe in any boat we were ever in. Oh she would get a fishing pole, but the same general conversation took place any time we went fishing, from the Everglades, lakes and rivers of Minnesota and Wisconsin, the whole West Coast, the East Coast, the Caribbean, Canada, you name it. I have been fishing everywhere, though the Cayman Islands were probably my favorite because I got to drink at the bar of the hotel with William "The Refrigerator" Perry and watch him eat, and man, that is something to see. Uh-oh, another digression.

This is my mother's concept of fishing with explicit instructions to my dad:

"Toots, would you please set up my line properly. I always screw it up." And my father would dutifully do her rod (and mine) because he really enjoyed all these aspects of fishing, which we did not.

Once the hooks were on, she would say, "Do me a favor and bait my hook, I don't want to get my hands all greasy from the bait." The bait were these small little live fish whose name I don't know but I thought they were really cool, flipping around in the water bucket all the time and then swimming alongside the boat when they were in the water on the hook.

"And go ahead and toss the line in for me. I'll take the rod from there and put it next to me."

Then when something would bite, she would say, "Toots, would you reel in that fish, I'm reading this book and I don't want to get all wet and slimy." And my father obliged without a peep not out of courtesy, but because he loved fishing and always got to fish with two lines at the same time. And the nickname 'Toots' came from a funky waitress at Joe's Stone Crab in Miami Beach who kept calling him that at a dinner once, and it stuck for about ten years or so. It was a nickname only my parents used, and I have no clue why they did that or what it means. But that's what they called each other for a long time.

So he would pull the fish in and the whole thing would start over exactly as above. Pretty much the same happened for me because I sure as hell couldn't set up my own rod, reel and line, but I did have the enthusiasm of bringing the fish in by myself, or almost by myself.

It was a warm day and we had a big lunch–my parents always have a big lunch when fishing–and by late afternoon we were all getting pretty tired and sunburned and my dad said we would have to paddle back soon. 'We' meaning those two. So he put my bait on the line and we gently lowered it into the water, drifting behind us as we gently rolled along, when after about 15 minutes I suddenly realized that my bait wasn't swimming any more. I lifted it out of the water, and it was just a sagging noodle. Dead.

I showed it to my father. "Well, Shane. I guess the bait is getting tired too."

I coyly answered, "He's dead, I think." Not that I really understood death then or even now, but it seemed like the right thing to say.

"Yup, he's dead. Go ahead, just toss it in the water."

This is one of those times where there was a "failure to communicate", maybe. It's a line from one of my parents' favorite movies, which I find incredibly boring. Whenever they watch it, they use the phrase "failure to communicate" for about a week and chuckle every time they say it. Tiresome at best. He wanted me to throw the dead baitfish in the water and keep fishing while we paddled back. I just wanted to go home. So I just took the whole rod and reel and threw the whole damn thing in the water. After all, that's what he said. It sank very slowly into the water, slow enough to make my father think he could reach it in time as he scrambled toward my side of the canoe. He quickly reached into the water trying to grab it, but it was just out of reach. He leaned more and more as it gently drifted downward until all his weight was off the side of the boat, and boom, the canoe went over, throwing everything into the water, worst of all me. It took awhile to get things sorted out and the boat righted (with a little help from some nice people nearby, who never stared at me once), but my dad didn't talk to me anymore until we made it back to the canoe rental place. Then he abruptly but quietly told me to never do that again. He was pretty pissed off, but wouldn't yell. I knew I had screwed up being a clown and I learned from it. I never threw my rod in the water ever again. Which was a good idea, since I doubt he would have ever taken me fishing again. You can only push your parents so far.

Chapter 3
The Vikings love BBQ

Later at the end of the summer, we drove way outside Minneapolis for some reason into farm country. My dad wanted to go to a special restaurant that he had heard about. It's called 'barbeque'. It's a lot of smoke and meat and I really don't have a taste for it. But he and my mom love that stuff. And he said he didn't believe there was good barbecue in Minnesota, so we all had to go and check it out. So we drove up to this little tiny building and even I could read the sign on it since it had a short name: "Lee's Ribs". There was an old pickup truck with a load of wood in it parked near the front. Smoke was coming out of a metal chimney. My dad looked at it and mumbled something about it looking like the real deal, but I don't know what he meant. When we walked in, I knew I was in the right place. There were black people there, my people! First of all, Lee was the nicest guy in the world, but his wife was super special–she treated me like the ladies in Miami. Since I didn't eat most of that crazy food they were making, she made up some special little plate for me and had me sit on her lap while I was eating. And they didn't even know us. Can't get nicer than that. But the really strange thing about the place was that it was small and had one really big table toward the side. I later found out when we went back that it was really just a bunch of small tables pushed together. Now get this. The whole place was empty except this big table with about a dozen guys at it. And there seemed to be mounds of that BBQ food filling up the whole table. I mean more meat than I had ever seen in one place in my life. I couldn't really see them well from my perch near the counter with Ms. Lee, but suddenly one of those guys stood up, and I'm telling you he was the biggest guy I ever saw in my life to that time. Later I got to ride on Moses Malone's shoulders and that's about the highest you can ride, but later, man, later. And then another guy got up and he was even bigger. And sure enough, it seemed the entire black population of Minnesota was eating BBQ in Lee's Ribs with us there too. And I realized then, that black people in Minnesota were so fucking big that they must have scared the crap out of everyone else, and that's why they kept to themselves–they didn't want to scare everyone all the time. At least that was my logic. My dad was looking at those guys and said, "This is pretty strange. Where the hell did all these black guys come from–we're in the middle of nowhere in Minnesota." And he looked and looked and mumbled, "These guys sort of look familiar. But I can't imagine I know them." Finally, one really big guy walked over to the counter for some sweet potato pie–now that was something I did like. He looked down at me and gave me a big, friendly smile, asked my parents if he could pick me up, and they smiled back and said sure. So he took my entire body in his hands and lifted me up over his head onto his shoulders and walked back to the table to introduce me to his friends. Well, they started tossing me around and playing and laughing and calling me 'little fella' and other affectionate nicknames. I told them my name and they were all yelling "Shanito" at me cause they thought that was the funniest name they ever heard. I mean these were great guys–I wanted to go to the park and hang out with them. After a little while, he brought me back to my parents and sat for a minute and they chatted briefly. He said I was a really cute and funny little kid. My dad seemed puzzled by the whole thing and finally asked him, "What exactly are you guys doing in this neck of the woods?"

The guy laughed and put out his hand. "My name is Alan, nice to meet you." And my dad gave him his strongest handshake so the big guy wouldn't think he was a wimp. Then Alan went on. "We're with the Minnesota Vikings. This is the only place in Minnesota where you can get real BBQ."

Then my dad looked over and realized he was looking at a whole bunch of future Hall of Fame football players and was beaming. Alan brought us over to introduce us and we met them all and they really were great guys. Famous guys, though I was too young to know that at the time–Alan Page, Jim Marshall, Carl Eller, and the rest. And they thought I was a cool kid, which made me feel very special. No one was staring at me.

Well, I saw a few of them again several times, cause we went to Lee's a lot and I guess they did too, but I never saw that big a group ever again. When they were playing on TV, my dad would point out the guys we met. It was pretty cool, but on TV you can't tell how big they are. We always had fun at Lee's. And Lee taught me one thing. I'm pretty sure he was from Mississippi and he was a smart guy, as was his wife. So I have to go back a little on my previous remarks about the educational system in Mississippi. Apparently, you can overcome it.

Chapter 4
A stranger saves us from the cold

Since we're on the subject of sports, I have another story to tell you. It took place during the winter of 1979-80, not the first winter we arrived, but the year after. That's because we ran away from Minnesota the first year when it got real cold, but I'll tell you about that shortly. I'm really not concerned about telling things out of order. I'm not a professional writer and the story about the Vikings reminded me about another sports story where I met a famous guy. My dad says my storytelling is like a writer named Proust, but since I can't read, except for sight-reading maybe a few hundred words, that name means nothing to me. But I'll take it as a compliment.

Anyway, it was the coldest fucking night I ever experienced in my time in Minnesota. It was like 20 or 30 degrees below zero with a wind chill around -50 degrees. I know this because it was on the TV weather, which I loved to watch. I always memorize the temperature numbers and I have a really good memory for numbers. It was so cold that it hurt to breathe. But the University of Minnesota hockey team had a home game and we were season ticket holders and there was no way we were going to miss that game. It may have been against their arch rival, Wisconsin, but I'm not sure. That's not important for the flow of the story.

What was important was the fact that we were still driving the VW pop-up camper van that my dumbshit father bought in Miami. Now that was one kickass car, especially when you're talking beaches, Miami, camping and all sorts of activities. Since we were poor then, he got an old one real cheap and had a friend fix it up. Elena did the curtains, which were very tasteful. It was not air-conditioned, which was mildly annoying in Florida. It did not have any heater, which was essentially insane living in the winter in Minnesota. That's not entirely true–there was a tiny amount of non-functional heat coming out of the defroster onto the front window. This was used to stuff gloves on to heat them up so we could constantly change to warmed up gloves for longer rides every 15 minutes or so. And we had to crack the windows so the windshield wouldn't fog up too much. What an idiot my dad was. So during winter months, whenever we went in it, I was stuffed into a mummy sleeping bag with a huge down coat, pants, boots, gloves, etc. to the point you could only see my eyes. And placed on the bed in the back. Which was bizarre but effective. I was pretty warm, though I felt like an idiot. My parents were up front freezing their asses off, which served them right for their inability to function like normal adults. When we arrived, the place was really crowded as expected, but we lucked out and got a pretty close parking spot. My dad's originally a New Yorker and prides himself on getting good parking spots. He said Minneapolis was a piece of cake for parking in comparison to NYC. I wouldn't know, nor did I care, because I wasn't walking a single stride in that weather–it was a 100% carry night, no questions asked. When we got to the arena, we got to the side where a whole area is an open facade (like I would know that word), and we immediately scurried under the brick roof to get out of the wind; my parents figuring they would work their way around to the fan entrances on the other side with minimal wind exposure. There were some guys in dark suits and overcoats at each end looking around but they didn't see us, and I'm pretty sure my parents knew we weren't supposed to be there, but they didn't give a rat's ass, we all needed to get out of the wind. Suddenly, this big black limousine pulls up right next to us and a couple of guys in the same overcoats get out, followed by some other people I couldn't see very well. Finally, a very distinguished looking gentleman got out and everyone was looking at him. The guys in the overcoats asked us to stand back away from the car, but the handsome looking guy brushed them aside and walked right over to us and put his hand out. My parents seemed clueless and shook his hand, while the guy talked about two sentences of hockey, how this was a big game and all that stuff. We then started to walk away and he called us back and said, "Come along with us and come through this side door and get out of the cold. It's a brutal night."

No need to say any more, we went right along with them and magically a door we couldn't even see suddenly opened and bam, we were right in the arena and not far from the long steps that led to our high up seats. The pleasant man shook our hands again and said it was nice to meet us and he gave me a special long handshake and rubbed my head. Being insightful, he said I was a very cute little guy. That was a nice thing to say but getting us into the arena without walking all the way around was a hell of a lot better and probably saved my fingers from falling off. I watched him walk away and he was led to some really great seats near the center of the rink. My mom and dad were speechless until I asked in my limited fashion who the hell that guy was. And my mom said, "His name is Walter Mondale and he's the Vice President of the United States. And I have no idea how they could let us get right up to him." Which again meant nothing to me at the time, but I liked watching the news with my parents and I studied it hard. And one day I saw him on TV and recognized him. I didn't really know what his job was, except that he was important and hung out with the President, who I did know was the head honcho. I always like knowing people who are on TV. I'm a celebrity sucker. Now I know that everyone hates politicians and blame them for everything wrong in the world. But I happen to know one politician who was really nice to strangers and saved me from freezing my butt off on the coldest night of the year. I'd vote for him anytime. And I always vote.

Chapter 5
Converting to Catholicism

Alright, now even I'm confused. Once I get going on sports stories I lose track of myself. Oh yeah, I gotta go back now to the fall when I started school in Minneapolis.

So the first summer ended, and I got enrolled in school. Despite being novices at this, my parents were pretty diligent and went to check out the school I had been placed in. So we all trudged down to this big building and went inside and met some woman, who asked if we wanted a tour, before meeting my new teacher. She seemed OK, but had the warmth of a Minnesota winter.

I first began to realize something was wrong when my mother's eyes started welling up with tears. She's a very emotional person, but this setting was an odd place for her to act up. But then even I started to notice some strange things. There were a lot of kids moving around the halls, presumably classes going to different activities, and it was quickly apparent that they were all handicappers. But the strangest part was that they all had very different handicaps, some of which I wasn't very familiar with. Some were blind, some were in wheelchairs with something called cerebral palsy as my dad later told me (and I later had several very good friends with that same problem), some were 'developmentally disabled' like me, though I didn't see many Downers around. It was a real hodgepodge. I never saw a collection of people with so many different handicaps in my life, before or since, except maybe at a Special Olympics meet. And the hall lights were dim, which made it feel even creepier. I don't remember much about the tour cause I kept watching my mom, who kept watching my dad, who kept staring at the lady giving us the tour. We all noticed that some of the teachers or aides were tapping the walls with a stick in rhythmic timing as the kids walked solemnly to wherever they were going. My dad later said it reminded him of a Roger Corman horror movie, but I have no idea who that guy is, and I hate horror movies. Except for all the Halloween and Friday the 13th movies, though I didn't like Halloween III very much, cause they left Michael Myers out. After a brief tour of pretty much nothing but halls, classrooms, an old gym and auditorium, we were taken to meet my new teacher. She seemed really nice and cheerful and was very nice to me and my parents. We looked in on the class and noticed the same thing–there were blind kids, cerebral palsy kids, one Downer and a few other disabled folks, and even a deaf kid. My dad asked about the program and according to him she said they just tried to keep everyone busy with activities, but it was hard to do since everyone was different and couldn't do different things. I guess my dad started getting annoyed and pushy, asking why a blind kid would be in the same class with a deaf kid in the same class as cerebral palsy and kids like me. He asked what kind of a program could be constructed that would fit all of them properly. I never got involved in the discussion, but I knew he thought there was something seriously wrong. The teacher said it was a difficult setting, but this was how the school district placed special education kids (new term for me – turned out I was called special ed, too). She also said that things worked out better than we could imagine and that I would be very happy there. Then she invited us to go with her as she took the class to the gym and we obliged, of course. No reason to be impolite.

She rounded up the class by gently rapping a long wooden stick against the wall and calling out to everyone that it was gym time. They all lined up along a wall just outside the classroom door, and began to walk almost soldier style, in rhythm with the tapping. As we walked, my dad asked, "What's with the stick rapping against the wall?" The teacher answered that it was a great tool to keep the attention of the kids, keep the blind kids oriented as to pace and direction, and even the deaf kid could see her tapping at a given pace. My dad simply said, "Well, that seems to be a well developed strategy to integrate all the kids into walking together. How utterly clever." The teacher smiled proudly.

We didn't stay long and once outside, my mom actually started crying, which was not something she did very much except during movies and frankly, I don't get the whole movie-crying thing. I have never cried during a movie. My dad looked pretty pissed off, too. I had no clue what the hell was going on. It didn't seem like the greatest place to go to school, but I was game for a shot and the teacher was young and sort of cool.

Everyone was quiet for a minute or so, until my dad said, "Well, now we have a problem. We have to find him a school, because there is not a chance in hell he is going to this piece of shit place." That's when I became Catholic for a while.

I guess my parents made lots of phone calls, but in the end, there really was no public school that they would accept. That was because there was no other place that was offered to me. So they found this private Catholic school and we went there and it seemed a lot brighter and happier and in my class at that school, there were just handicappers with problems like me and they had things like speech therapy, life skills (that's about making it through the day with as few problems as possible), sports, learning to write and do numbers, and the like. Essentially my future curriculum for a long time, since I'm a slow learner and I needed to get those skill sets down if I was going to be a success in life. I'm not saying they didn't have these things at the first school. I just don't think we ever got to that conversation in detail.

The funniest thing about the Catholic school was the clothes all the teachers wore. They were called nuns, and we called them sisters. We weren't related in any way, but we still called them sisters. Pretty crazy, huh. But I tell you, those sisters could run their asses off in the playground even with all their strange clothes on. I had seen nuns before in a Catholic church a few times in Miami when Elena would take me to church and they sort of scared me then, with their heads all covered and the whole huge black and white gown stuff and big clunky shoes. But I really liked the place and had a pretty good time. Of course this is relative because I had never been to any school before, and I later realized they were missing things like good music and dancing, funny games and such, but all-in-all I was a pretty happy guy when I got on the bus each morning and when I got off at the end of the day as well. We had 'prayer' time each day, but since I didn't know what prayers or God were, it was one of those times I just meditated. I didn't know I was meditating. I just knew you had to keep your mouth shut and listen or pretend to listen to whatever the person in the front was saying and not make a peep. So I just relaxed and thought about good stuff like what was on TV that night or maybe tried to guess what lunch would be. That's sort of like meditating, I think. I found that time very mellow and actually looked forward to it.

I don't have a lot of stories to tell about that school,

because I just can't remember much about it. I know I enjoyed it, but I still have no distinct memories of people or kids. None of us can even remember the name of the school. Really. Isn't that odd? Well, it didn't matter, because I only went there the first year for a few months, until my parents had their little huffy fit and things changed abruptly.

Chapter 6
The Cold Sucks

My dad was a doctor then, spent most of his life as a doctor, and now is retired. He always said he wanted to achieve my lifestyle after I retired, which I did around 1996. As he explained it to me and as he will point out now, he was sort of a doctor then–a very young doctor. He was a 'resident' in Miami, came to Minneapolis and wanted to be a specialist, a more advanced doctor and was going to start more medical training at the University of Minnesota the next July to become a different kind of doctor. This is not my area of expertise, so I have to go with his version.

Around October, it started getting cold. I mean really cold. I had never experienced anything like it, but you got to wear really cool immense puffy jackets, pants, gloves, boots, and hats and I liked it. Until it snowed once. Never saw anything like it. Just white crap coming from the sky and piling up on the ground. I now know that kids around the world love snow, love playing in the snow, having snowball fights (I did like that), building snowmen (I did not like that), making snow angels, building snow forts. All sorts of neat stuff to them. And they can have it for the most part. Because there was no fucking way I was ever going to put one of my feet in that white shit. That's right, I absolutely refused to walk in snow. I would walk on a shoveled sidewalk or road, which they did pretty efficiently in Minneapolis, but my tootsies were never going to be lost from my sight into the white morass (not my word). This did not sit well with my parents, who were pretty fed up from their years carrying me everywhere. But I was now not only the master of the 'going limp' strategy, but had developed a new wrinkle called the 'endless squirm'. That's when they are holding you and try to gently put you down in a standing position in preparation for walking. I was pretty strong in my own way, and at the merest hint of being put down to walk, I would wriggle my entire body until the person could no longer hold onto me and was forced to gently let me plop down on the sidewalk or ground. And there I would sit with an angry look, arms crossed, and not the least intention of assuming the standing position. As frustrated as my parents became, I became even more adamant. It wasn't a standoff, it was a victory. They are such softies. Accordingly, I never walked in snow until the following year, and I didn't do much of it the second and last year in Minneapolis either.

It wasn't just one thing, but a whole collection of things that occurred that fall, that finally resulted in my parents abandoning ship. They didn't like the cold either. And they didn't like the school I was in very much, though they and I were thankful we even found that one. My mom wasn't going to begin school at the University until the following September. And my dad wanted some free time before he started back to training as a radiologist. So one day in November, we had a serious meeting to discuss our immediate future over dinner. I was naturally accorded a seat at the table, but I don't believe I was allowed a vote. This changed when I got older, but I will allow that my youth and general confusion over life made my loss of voting rights a reasonable decision. Didn't matter though. I would have voted along with them anyway.

My dad said, in his most articulate manner, "This whole thing blows. We gotta get out of here." My mom concurred wholeheartedly and a firm strategy was put in place. We were leaving in December and not coming back until the temperature surpassed 55 degrees in the spring. We loaded up the VW van and went......................... back to MI-AMI!!

Chapter 7
Fleeing to Miami

Since we were poor, my parents were dysfunctional at life, and my dad refused to work until July, housing was seemingly an issue. But unbeknownst to me, they had the perfect plan, which was well coordinated and flawlessly thought out. Our beloved VW van made the trip effortlessly and was parked for about 4 months in the driveway of Elena and Hector. My parents slept in the van and used the house as much as they wanted. I got MY OWN BEDROOM in the house, the first one I ever had to myself. It was so cool being back 'home'. When we arrived, there must have been over 50 people, all my favorite lady friends, park playmates, park domino players, musicians playing guitars, and a true Cuban feast to celebrate our return. I had a giant bowl of steaming malanga shoved in my face almost immediately and I wolfed it down. What a welcoming party! I had more lipstick smeared on my face from all the kisses that I looked like a clown. Even my mom and dad had red cheeks and all of us had sore ribs from endless hugging. Man, it is so great to see your best friends after a long separation. And it was warm!!

My bedroom was spectacular, though as you will read later, not quite as spectacular as the one I later had in Philadelphia. But it had dozens of stuffed animals, toys, a great large bed to jump on and other fashionable appointments, which were unfamiliar but very comfortable to me. I could not stop smiling, and neither could my parents. These were some of the greatest people I have ever known in my life.

Naturally things settled down somewhat in a week or so, but the Cuban culture is an outgoing one, and there was always boisterous laughing and yelling and singing and all sorts of shenanigans going on. And especially eating, because Elena was one hell of a cook. My mom became a great Cuban cook during our stay, as Elena was also a good teacher. Her first task was to perfect black beans Cuban-style which sounds easier than it is. She and Elena would each make a pot and taste it, with my mom's getting tossed pretty quickly the first week or so. When she made some progress, it was decided that both pots would be put on the dinner table when Hector got home and he would get to choose which one stayed for dinner, without knowing who made it. For a couple of weeks he would sneer after tasting my mom's and say, "You need mucho more practice." Then we'd all laugh. But after a few more weeks, he started having trouble telling them apart and finally, some nights he would pick my mom's as the winner. Which pissed off Elena a little, but in a good-natured way. Then on to seafood and chicken enchilada Cuban-style (sort of like a creole recipe, not the Mexican kind), flan, paella, platanos, and a bunch of other foods. But my mom never would make the malanga for me–I got it directly from Elena the whole time, which was fine with me.

Things were working out so well, that it became clear we might lose my father forever. You see, in the late 1970's in Miami, the Cuban culture was very sexist (see, I can be very politically observant). Women were supposed to be homemakers and take care of the men first and most specially, which was just fine with me and my dad. My dad had never experienced the beauty parlor life first hand and he quickly realized this was the dream life. He would sleep in the van until maybe 10 am, and then there would be a gentle knock on the door. And in the sweetest, gentlest voice Elena would almost whisper in heavily accented English, "Bob, time to get up. I have your breakfast." And he would groggily open the door to find a silver tray with fresh Cuban coffee, fresh fruit, and an array of pastelitos. This was virtually every day!! Then he would wander into the house later and the women would fawn all over him (not quite as enthusiastically as me, but close), bringing in all sorts of foods and casseroles for him to taste. He'd drink Cuban coffee all day, then nap in the afternoon to prepare for a massive, spectacular dinner at night. The man must have gained 20 pounds while we were there. Had the offer been made (maybe it was and I didn't know about it), I truly believe he would have stayed there for life under those conditions. My mom would yell at Elena to stop spoiling my dad, but she would just laugh and say that maybe my mom should be serving my dad breakfast in bed in the van. Well, that would always turn my mom's face purple and she would just say, "He can dream on." Not that my mom never brought my dad a breakfast in bed for special occasions or when he had the flu. But she could not abide this royalty treatment and even asked my dad to put a stop to it. He slyly replied, "There's no need to insult their good intentions. I can put up with it."

In February, it was my birthday, and when I woke up and looked in the backyard, there was a fucking circus there. I'm not talking a clown and a musician. I'm talking a veritable circus. Ponies to ride, musicians, jugglers, clowns, magicians, acrobats, belly dancers–you name it. By noon there must have been over 100 people there. Never had more fun or presents in my life. A party to beat all parties for a little kid. Only matched by my 21st birthday that is a story unto itself. I ate till my belly almost burst, got a great winter sunburn, and laughed so much my ribs hurt. Same for my mom and dad and essentially my entire 'second' family. It was a completely perfect day except for one minor disagreement. The ponies. Everyone loved the ponies and everyone had cameras to take pictures of me on the pony. They bought and dressed me in a fucking cowboy outfit–full leather and fringe. I finally looked like Alan Ladd in the movie, "Shane". Actually pretty cool duds. This was a problem though, since I was scared shitless to sit on a pony. Imagine that–a Mongol scared to ride his pony. How utterly ironic. I have no idea why, when I look back on it, but I simply could not get on the pony. I could pet it, feed it a carrot, rub its nose and all that, but I simply would not get on it. People were begging me to get on the damn pony and I used every trick in my arsenal including going limp and my uncontrollable squirm to avoid the hazard. In retrospect, I think I disappointed people, but my dad says he and everyone there thought it was the funniest thing in the world. These people don't understand funny.

Chapter 8
When my parents abandoned me

In early March, my parents abandoned me. Yes, you read that right. They up and left me. I had no clue where they went. They tried to tell me, but I couldn't understand. In fact, I didn't understand a single thing they were trying to say the night before they left. They gave me big hugs and kisses at bedtime that night and my mom had a few tears. I simply woke up and they were gone. The van was still there, but they were gone. I looked around for them awhile and couldn't find them. I went up to Elena and asked where they were and she smiled and said they were 'away' like we talked about last night. Now what the fuck did that mean? Away? And everyone in the house was walking around as if nothing had happened out of the ordinary. I got my usual breakfast, the beauty parlor opened, all the ladies were happy as usual, Elena was humming songs, Elena's kids came home from school and played with me awhile, and finally Hector got home from work. Usual big dinner. TV afterwards. Everyone happy. No one even mentions the fact that my parents were gone! I was puzzled since this had never happened before. Admittedly, I wasn't THAT unhappy due to the fact I was totally spoiled by Elena's entire family, all her relatives and friends, and my life was never better, but I did love my parents as any kid does. And to have them do this to me was simply an insult. No respect whatsoever.

Late that night just before we were in bed, my parents called on the phone to talk to me. My mom was all teary and said she missed me terribly already. And mentioned that they were in New York City. NYC!! I knew about NYC, though not like I did later in life when I was an integral part of the art scene there and was a judge at the Coney Island Mermaid Parade–but once again I am getting ahead of myself.

So we had sort of a conversation and then I heard the words weeks and months, and I'll be honest with you, I didn't have a very good sense of time at that age. It wasn't like I could read a calendar then. So I really didn't have any idea when they were coming back, but it gradually dawned on me that they were coming back. I mean, they were at least calling and staying in touch. I just didn't know when they would get their asses back to Miami. At this point in the story, the next couple of months go murky and I will yield to my father's explanation to me of what transpired for him and my mother, though in minimal detail, since this is my autobiography. Briefly, he and my mom took advantage of an opportunity to travel around the world for a couple of months. Turns out there was this airline that no longer exists (Pan Am–I flew it a couple of times–nice service as opposed to today), that sold an around the world ticket for $999, with as many stops as you wanted as long as you didn't backtrack. Yup, my parents abandoned me for a god-dam extended vacation. Turns out they were smart, because once my dad started studying to become an x-ray doctor, he never got any time to do that sort of thing ever again. And apparently they had a lot of fun and showed me all sorts of pictures from the trip. They are interesting, but frankly, I was and still am happy they left me in Miami. Bunch of weird looking people and places (no Mongols), weird food, pictures of old buildings, cities, villages, farms, boats. You get the picture–strange places with no friends, though they claim to have made a few. I settled into my perfect life with Elena and the family quickly and to this day am thankful I did not have to endure going to interesting foreign places, despite the fact I am a seasoned traveler. But gimme NYC, SF, Miami, Chi-town, Philly–places where I know the lay of the land. Sure a quick tropical vacation like the Caribbean is OK, but world travel was never on my top ten list.

But once I realized they really were coming back, that was all I needed to know. My anxiety subsided and I lived my usual life of Riley until they did come back. To be honest, I settled in so well that I pretty much didn't think much about them except when they would call once a week. I trusted them–they're good people. In one of my earliest forms of parental torment, I generally would get on the phone for about a minute and then tell them I was busy and hand the phone to whoever was near me and go off and do my thing. I know that really pissed them off. My dad says that's called passive-aggressive behavior. I wouldn't know, but it made me laugh, so I did it. Sometimes they pleaded to get me back on the phone, and if I agreed, you could hear my mom's emotional torture through the phone. Ha! Serves 'em right for romping off. And that's just about all I have to say about that except that when they came back, it was party time again, and I had no qualms about it. And at the time of their return, it turns out that the temperature had hit 55 degrees in Minneapolis, so it was time to go back to the frigid wilderness.

Chapter 9
Best breakfast – Best blues

So back we went to Minneapolis. My dad started going into the university hospital everyday for something called a 'residency program', essentially meaning he was studying medical stuff and pictures. My mom was going to the University of Minnesota studying something, but I have no clue what the hell she was doing except reading a lot at night. And I returned to the fold of Catholicism at the school with the nuns and a few priests. Turns out I liked that school and though it was by no means exciting, they were good folks and treated me fair and square. I may not know much about religion and Catholicism in particular, but based on my experiences at that school, those Catholics were solid.

My dad had found this really cool apartment with lots of glass windows that overlooked the Mississippi River and was just across a bridge from the University of Minnesota in an area called Cedar-Riverside. It was cool for lots of reasons. It had something called 'diversity'. Which means there were all different kinds of people there, which we all liked. One day, we came out of the building and in walked a BLACK person! We couldn't believe it. It was this young girl who was really tall with a beautiful smile. She was in high school. Pretty soon we got to know her, her sisters, brother and mother, who was a very smart lady who taught at the university. Bam–we had babysitters!! And they were the best. They didn't babysit, they took me out all over the place. Some weekend days, we would be strolling around Dinkytown, a really funky hippie area in those days, and bump into my parents who would ask where we were going, and then I would ask where they were going. We would chat amiably for a minute or two and each would go on their own way. It made me feel very adult-like. Very independent. And my parents loved the Berry sisters, cause when they called to see if anyone was available to hang with me, there were enough of them that someone would always be around. Freedom for me, freedom for them. And the Berry sisters just cracked me up. They made me laugh, rode me around on their bicycles, and we just cruised everywhere, especially my favorite area, Dinkytown.

Now if you're familiar with Minneapolis at all, there is no need to even discuss Dinkytown at that time. It was the cultural focal point (my dad's term, of course) of the university area. Meaning lots of hippie places, hippie people, hippie students. You get the picture. We all loved Dinkytown. Lots of good places to eat, real cheap, too. And best of all, there was Al's Breakfast. It's a famous place, you can look it up on Wikipedia (I have my own computer in my room now). But it's difficult to make a reader understand the real feel of the place back then. Most important was Al himself, who we got friendly with because we went there at least twice a week for a year. He was a great guy who always was very stoic looking and seemingly quiet, but on the sly he had a great sense of humor and would always do something funny with me whenever I dropped in. And the other people behind the counter all looked like hippies and were the friendliest people in the world. Ignoring the fact they made the best breakfasts in the world, they were hysterical. I had a little act going that I would do with one of the women at the counter. I keep saying counter, which probably gives you a mistaken image of the place. There was nothing but a counter. Al's is about 20 feet wide. There were like a dozen or so stools at the counter and that's it. People waited in line out the door onto the street to eat breakfast starting at some insane hour like 5:30 am or so, and at 12 noon the door was locked. I don't mean around 12 noon. At EXACTLY 12 noon, the door was locked and if you were not inside the door, forget about it, you weren't getting breakfast that day. No discussion allowed. People would sit at the counter and then another row of people would stand behind them at their stools. When someone finished and got up, the next person in line got that stool. So the way it worked, you might think that you would get separated from your family and friends when you got your stool. But Al and the workers were too smart for that. When a stool opened up, my mom would usually take it first. Then when the next stool opened up, say, four stools away, everyone in between would move one place over–I mean they had to move their butts, their food, their coffee and all. That would free up two stools next to each other and I would sit next to my mom. Finally a third stool would open up, the scene would repeat itself and we would end up sitting together, although we would be at various stages of eating. Things could only be coordinated to a certain level. And this wasn't anything special for us–this is how it worked for everyone. Except sometimes if the open stools were at each end of the counter and it was too much trouble to move everyone. Then you just let the person behind you go ahead and waited for a closer stool.

Anyway, one day, this really cool waitress asked if she could hold me because, as I may have previously mentioned, I was a stud little kid. My parents were only too happy to send me across the counter and handed me right over. Suddenly she headed to the back kitchen with me, where they washed stuff and had dishes, pots, and pans–it was out of sight of the customers, as opposed to the front grill that was right at the front window and door. Next thing you know, she handed me to another beauty and started throwing pots and pans all over the place and then we all started banging them together, making a real ruckus. And then she left and went back to waitressing the counter without me, completely ignoring my parents as if nothing had happened. Well, everyone in the place (I think maybe a couple of dozen people between the people with seats and those standing behind the stools) started cracking up, as did my parents. After a minute or so, my dad said he asked her if I was coming back. She said I had a small accident and they were working to clean up the blood–this is the story I was told. More laughter. The act was well received and it would be resurrected occasionally when we saw that waitress and it always got a laugh. I got to hang out in the back with beautiful women for 5 minutes or so and my parents got a humorous break from me. Al's was the best place to eat, and made the best pancakes I have ever tasted.

The other great place my parents used to take me was the Cedar-Riverside Cafe. Mostly on Friday nights. We could walk there from our place, but that was a damn long trip in winter. There were a lot of bars and stuff along the way to the place, and during the winter we would stop into several of these places every 100 feet or so to have a hot cider, so we could make it to the next place and so on. My parents got whiskey in their hot cider and they were usually pretty drunk by the time we got to the Cafe itself, which didn't have alcohol if I remember correctly.

Now the Cedar-Riverside Cafe was special because it had music that all three of us loved. The blues. We all love the blues. And the music was live–yup, real singers and musicians, not records. It was usually this guy named Spider John Koerner, who I think is just great. While my dad and I were writing this book, I remembered it all of a sudden and wanted to hear him again so we brought him up on YouTube. Seems he doesn't sing the blues anymore, he's a folk singer now. That's OK, because even though I don't like folk music that much (can't dance to it at all), I liked seeing him again, though he looks even older than my dad now. I learned that he stopped singing the blues when he realized he wasn't black–it was in an interview that my dad watched and explained to me. I can relate to that since as I have already told you, I am black even though I look white. Well, I can relate to him feeling black, but I can't understand why he switched back to white. Whatever. He had different people play with him on different nights, but usually a guy named Willie McGee was there too. But sometimes they had this really nice (and very beautiful) woman sing and play guitar with them. She was a little famous then, but became very famous later on. Her name was Bonnie Raitt. We have a lot of her music on our computers. And though I bet she doesn't remember me, I remember her very well, because she would always wave and smile at me whenever she saw me (I think she just thought I was cute), and sometimes would even come over and sit with us when they took a break, for a couple of minutes, and chat with me and my parents. She liked to put me on her lap and take my chair and I loved it. I still see her on TV to this day and I think that's pretty cool. It was so much fun to listen to them in that tiny cafe standing just a few feet from us. And it was free! I could get up and just dance and no one paid me any mind, except for maybe a few smiles, because everyone there looked like hippies. I mean, it was a pretty small cafe for music–but probably my all-time favorite music place.

Chapter 10
I make no apologies for wrestling

Perhaps the two most important cultural events of my life occurred in Minneapolis that would forever change my view of entertainment. It was my introduction to professional wrestling and separately, to the Rocky movies.

I am well aware that virtually every 'developmentally disabled' kid in the world loves professional wrestling. I go and I see. Olympic and college wrestling is lame, though I later became good friends with Morris Johnson who was an NCAA national wrestling champion at San Jose State. But that was later in Philly, and I gotta say he is one of the coolest dudes I ever met–but he is not Hulk Hogan. The reason I know about wrestling and handicapped people is that my dad took me to a match (this was before WWE) with a friend of his, Morey. Morey was a scientist who studied genes. I learned a little about genes much later–they make your hair color, eye color, how big you are and that sort of thing. But Morey said he liked the whole feel of wrestling matches and in particular, said that when he went to one wrestling match, he could see more genetic abnormalities in that one place than he could see anywhere else in 10 years.

That's pretty funny when you think about it. My dad said Morey was a real character and liked him a lot. And get this, Morey later stopped being a scientist and moved away to run his family's ladies underwear store in a big city. He only intended to stay for a short time, but ended up liking it more than being a scientist and stayed there for good, as far as I know. So much for scientists.

At my first wrestling match, I simply knew this would be my lifelong passion as a fan. For some people, it's golf, baseball, football, basketball, soccer or hockey and I am also an avid fan of college basketball and pro baseball, but let me just spell it out here and now. Give me the number of any Wrestlemania, and I can tell you the city or cities, the attendance, the main matches, the announcers, and a whole bunch of other information. I simply know and love wrestling. You can analyze it and say it is not a sport, but you would be mistaken. These are great athletes–Morris told me he personally wrestled with some of these guys who went on to become WWE pros. He said they were good college wrestlers, though he claims to have beaten them all. I'll give him a pass on that.

How can anyone not like wrestling!! The guys are studs. The babes are incredible. They fight in cages, smash each other with tables and chairs, and yell and scream till their veins are bulging out everywhere. Good guys become bad guys, bad guys become good guys, wrestlers who hate each other become tag team partners, tag team partners become mortal enemies. Even the managers and announcers are hysterical. Now that is entertainment. Wrestling is my passion, has been for my entire life since Minneapolis, and I make no apologies for it. More on that later.

The other thing was seeing the Rocky movie. I knew immediately this was a great movie and when they started making more of them, I was in heaven, especially Rocky III with Hulk Hogan starring as ThunderLips. I have owned and worn out two sets of VHS tapes of all the Rocky movies, several sets of the DVD's and still watch a Rocky movie probably once a week. I watch wrestling probably 3 or 4 times a week and have a collection of well over 200 wrestling DVD's. And I know the specific info on each and every one of those DVD's. I know exactly where each and every DVD is placed in the DVD towers that house my collection. If you're going to be a fan, you gotta do it right.

My parents do not share my enthusiasm for wrestling but they performed their parental duties admirably by taking me to my fair share of matches over the years. They liked the first few Rocky movies, but lost interest after that. But let's face it. My dad listens to jazz and my mom is a painter who looks at art books. That is not entertainment.

Chapter 11
One phone call and we were outta there

So things started settling down in Minneapolis and though it didn't have the color and flavor of Miami, I liked it well enough. We got season tickets to the university basketball and hockey games and I loved that stuff. The basketball team had a whole bunch of guys who became pro's and I got to watch them for years–Kevin McHale, Trent Tucker and get this, Dave Winfield, who became one of my favorite Yankees, played basketball there too. And the hockey team had a coach and several players who became famous in the 1980 Olympics. I thought that was pretty cool. They didn't know me, but I sure as hell knew them.

But as winter settled in, I could see my parents becoming a bit despondent (I love that word he chose–it's big and when he explained it meant a little sad, I thought it was perfect for the story). None of us liked the cold weather or snow. My god, we were coming from Miami. I was probably the least affected by it, but it wore on me as well. But my dad said we were locked in for three years, and there wasn't much we could do about it. Until the phone call.

One night, one really cold night and it was snowing too,

92

we were sitting around watching TV and the phone rang. It was February–I remember because it was just after my birthday party. My mom got it and called to my dad and said someone was calling from San Francisco. They each gave the other a strange look and my dad shrugged his shoulders and took the phone. I watched him because he was in the kitchen and I was making a PB&J sandwich, or rather, he was making me a PB&J sandwich with the phone balanced on his shoulder, since I hadn't learned how to make my own sandwich yet. He said almost nothing (which is highly unusual for him) and just listened. After about 5 minutes with him only saying a few words here and there, he asked if they could hold on for a minute. I watched him as he put his hand over the phone speaker and called out to my mom, who turned down the TV.

He called out to her, "Do you want to move to San Francisco at the end of June?"

My mom smiled and nodded yes, without saying a word.

My dad got back on the phone and told them yes, and said he would call some person the next day.

That was the entire conversation that took place regarding our family decision to move to San Francisco. I was not even consulted, though in fairness, I was not familiar yet with the city of San Francisco. The only thing I knew was the San Francisco Giants and if they had a baseball team, I figured it must be a good place. My mom and dad sat me down and said we were moving there and that I would like it. As far as I was concerned, I was going wherever they were going. I wasn't exactly independent, so it was a moot point. But I appreciated their encouragement.

After the call, my mom and dad became very excited. I later learned my dad had screwed things up a couple of years before, due to their self-indulgent trip around the world. He can fill in the details here so I can move the story to its next setting in San Francisco. Seems we were originally supposed to move to SF after Miami. No one told me. But my dad wanted to hang out and do the world trip thing and delay going to the University of California, San Francisco for a year. Well, the people at UCSF said absolutely NO when he asked to delay coming for a year. I'm pretty sure they thought he was a nut. He asked if he could reapply for the next year and they said sure, but that there was no way he was going to get accepted. And sure enough, they bagged his ass and rejected him the second time and we ended up in Minneapolis. But now, they were calling him for the third time to see if he would change his job and come to them. Apparently some resident quit their job there, and they needed a warm body (that's how my dad put it). Since they knew him already, they made the call. Isn't it funny how things sometimes work out a long time after you think you've screwed it up?

Now don't get me wrong. I am not dissing the city of Minneapolis. As I said, I made some good friends there and 99% of the people treated me fine and proper. I had some good times. But let's face it. Minneapolis is not San Francisco for young studs like my family. People in Minneapolis likely would not agree. Everyone in Minneapolis thinks it is the greatest city in the world and sincerely so. My dad says that's because everyone who doesn't like it leaves as fast as they can. But I gotta say I didn't shed a tear when we moved to San Francisco, one of the great cities of the world. Little did I know how much I would like it.

The San Francisco Years

Chapter 1
Fancy food and great people

When we headed into San Francisco in the van for the first time, I noticed it was beautiful right off. I have an artistic streak in me. I can tell beauty, especially natural beauty better than most. I am mesmerized by the ocean, rainbows, lightning, mountains, desert and rolling hills. SF seemed like the real deal to me right off. And it was warm! Well, I thought it was warm that day we drove in, but then I learned about fog. I think fog looks very cool, but it's sort of cold. Fortunately not Minnesota cold, so I learned to like it. And yes, I am quite sophisticated in architecture as well, and clearly, this was a stunning city. I was a happy guy when we pulled up to our new home, which was smack dab in the middle of a trendy district called the Marina. It wasn't actually our home, we rented it. And only the bottom floor. It was sort of small, but my parents seemed happy, which made me happy, and it turned out to be a fine few years.

On the first day there, we went to the park by the water and watched kite fighters. Never saw anything like it–guys had kites way up in the air and they were fighting with each other–the kites, not the guys. Trying to cut the other kite's strings. I was mesmerized. My dad explained the whole thing to me but I didn't quite get it. Then the guys finished and after watching me staring at their skill for like a half hour, came over and showed me their kites and explained everything to me and showed me how the kites were made and what they were doing. Showing me something always works better than trying to explain it with words. I think that's sort of true for everyone. And they didn't stare at me or anything. They talked to me just like everyone else and were real friendly, too. I told my dad we needed to get one of those things immediately, but he just laughed and said he didn't know how to do that sort of stuff. At least he was honest about it. But we did get regular kites and flew them a lot at that park the first couple of years. I really loved the Marina.

We lived one block off a funky business street called Chestnut Street, which became my new Dinkytown, only better. There were all sorts of eating places, bars, pizza, grocery stores, a great deli and even a movie theater that showed pictures of naked women. I loved looking at the posters on the side of the entrance, but my parents never took me there to see a movie—what prudes! The movies had strange names that I had trouble reading because they all had a lot of X's in them. All of them did—pretty weird. I got to know a lot of the people who worked on that street. Everyone was so friendly, I felt like I was in Miami again—or at least a little.

There was this really cool guy named Angelo, who lived down the block from us, only he owned his own house, both floors. That's because he owned and was the chef at the best Italian restaurant any of us had ever been to before or since. It was called La Pergola. We went there one of our first nights in town to celebrate our arrival, and the whole place treated me and my parents so special. We never really figured out why except that they were great people—like

I told you–people are different and some people are just naturally good. Now this was a fancy restaurant. Everyone dressed up, people came in limos, even some famous people went there that my dad recognized over the few years (we saw the governor there once, but I can't remember his name), but we looked like bums because we were dressed like....... bums. We got there late that first night, which was a good thing. My dad said we never would have gotten a table except people were starting to finish up their meals. But no one seemed to care and the hostess who seated us said I was adorable and gave me a little hug. That was Ms. Angelo. Anyway, I thought my dad's eyes were going to bug out when he saw the prices on the menu, but he was in a celebration mood and seemed his usual oblivious. We had a great dinner and ended up as the very last people in the restaurant. That's when the other hostess came over and started talking to my dad and they talked about us just moving there and all sorts of stuff I didn't understand. Then she found out that we lived down the street from Angelo and it turned out that she was his daughter-in-law, Toni. Next thing you know, Angelo is chatting at the table in a sweat suit (he always wore a sweat suit when he was leaving the restaurant), calling us neighbors and picking me up and playing with me–I thought it was really cool to see a chef in a sweat suit instead of a white outfit and a silly hat like on TV. Then another chef guy comes out and it's his son, Jeff. And there was even another son, Greg who was working there–a real family place. Well, that's how we became regulars at La Pergola, a restaurant my father couldn't afford because he still wasn't a real doctor. But it didn't matter because I think Angelo knew that. He told my dad (a story related to me years later) to always come late when the place was clearing out and that he would take care of us. And he surely did. My dad never ever had to pay for MY food ever and half the time we or even just my parents ate there, there wouldn't even be a bill or maybe just half a bill. Toni and Jeff were very cool and since we usually were the last people there, they'd lock the door and we would crank up the music system and play rock instead of the usual mellow background stuff. Jeff would take us into the kitchen and make special desserts for my parents, crack open bottles of wine and they'd smoke cigarettes and drink till late into the night. We all really liked them, and years later, they even came out to visit us in Philly. Even the waiters became friends, though my favorite was Dominic, who always gently pinched my cheek whenever we came in. He was very serious looking when he worked, except when he saw me and would always give me a big smile.

Now get this. Besides Angelo being so nice to us at his restaurant, just about every month he would appear at our door in his sweat suit on a Sunday morning, with a box of fresh Italian pastries. He used to get them delivered every weekend to his house from some great bakery and then he'd drop a box off to us whenever he felt like it, which like I said was about once or maybe even twice a month (well, that's what my father is writing down and I think he is accurate on this). Can you imagine that happening today? A bunch of bums go into a fancy restaurant a couple of days after moving into a new city knowing no one, and the next thing you know, you're eating there almost free, the owner and his kids become friends, and then he's personally delivering pastries to us on weekend mornings. They don't make people like that anymore. Uh-uh–no way. Just doesn't happen. Maybe it's because Angelo was from a place called Italy. My parents talk about it sometimes and always say it was because of me. They all liked ME! My dad said if they had gone in without me that first night, no one would have noticed them at all. Now THAT makes me feel special. But I think they liked my mom and dad too. I made lots of friends on Chestnut Street, but Angelo and his family were my favorites.

Chapter 2
I'm no fighter, but I ain't no wimp

So my first few days in SF were pretty fantastic. I met the burrito guy, the Polish deli guy, the guys at Lucca deli, the waiters in tuxedos at Joe's, and got used to eating great pasta at E'Angelo's as well, right around the corner from our flat (that's another word for apartment). It was eating heaven and my dad got a lot fatter when we lived in San Francisco. And then we would head up to Union Street for more food and gelato ice cream in between, and all sorts of stuff. It was pretty crazy for that first week or two.

Then reality hit and my dad had to go to work everyday, which was a bummer, but my mom and I cruised around for the rest of the summer, always finding interesting stuff to do. Lots of cafes. I won't bore you with details since it was just running around having fun and seeing new things. No essential life details.

The real important stuff started in late August, when it was time for me and my mom to start school. Naturally, we went to different schools, but we had to enroll, which means you have to join. My mom and I went to my school, and I immediately knew I was home. I was in a special class that had several kids who sort of looked a lot like me, but I paid them no mind. Because when I went out to general recess on the playground, there were TONS of kids who had slanted eyes like me and it made me feel a real part of the community. They called them Chinese, Korean, and Japanese. No one called them Mongoloid. And no one called them Chinoid, Koreoid, or Japanoid–people are funny like that. And they weren't even in special classes like me. They were great at kickball, which was my second favorite sport at the time, and I was pretty good, too. The other Down kids weren't, so I got to play in a lot of important big-time games at that school yard with the kids who weren't in my special class for slow learners. It pays to have talent.

My teacher was a cool lady, but I don't remember a lot of specific things that happened in the class. I just remember I liked it and looked forward to my bus ride to school every day. I do remember that I had my first schoolyard fist fight at that school. And you won't believe this: I only had one real fistfight ever again in a schoolyard and that was in Philly like 10 years later and it was almost the same exact thing. In both cases, I was minding my own business, bouncing a big red rubber ball up and down since I knew dribbling was an important skill for basketball, which I liked a lot. And I wanted to get good at basketball in the worst way. Also, I needed to work on my ball catching skills and catching a bouncing ball was not so easy for me in those days. I screwed up often and would drop the ball, and accidentally smack it or kick it all the way to the schoolyard fence. Then, I would run over to retrieve it, return to my place in the middle of the yard, and start bouncing some more. I am easily entertained and could do this by myself for the entire recess without ever getting bored. Sort of like now when I can spend an hour just shooting baskets with a basketball–but in SF, I still couldn't even throw the ball up high enough to reach the basket. Well, one day, the ball rolled over to the fence and by the time I got there, this other bigger kid had grabbed my ball. He told me to buzz off, it was his ball now. It was probably my first real lesson in bullying. Now I am not a big or tough guy. I was pretty shrimpy in those days especially. But my dad had drilled boxing into me for years (with and without the famous red boxing gloves) and had always told me to never let kids push me around. I think he thought I was always going to get bullied because I was small, and I couldn't speak properly, and I was, well, 'handicapped'. I think he really worried about that a lot. I never really thought about it ever, cause I didn't even know what bullying was back then. But this kid was an asshole. I simply looked him in the face, extended my arms out to him and said, "Gimme my ball back". He was bigger than me (almost everyone was bigger than me) and I looked around for a teacher to help, but couldn't find one. I would like to say I knew karate or had some great strategy that I had learned, but that wasn't true. I was in new territory here. The kid ignored me and turned his back on me. I walked around him and again asked him to his face to give me the damn ball back, only I did it politely. Then the kid laughed at me, called me a retard, and pushed me in the chest and I fell to the ground and scraped my knees–real strawberries. I wasn't much of a crying kid and it really didn't hurt much. So I got up and faced the kid again, who was holding onto that ball real tight with both hands. Which in retrospect was quite an advantage, because I hauled off and nailed him with two punches in the mouth and took my ball back. The twerp just sat on the ground and starting bawling like a little baby until the teachers finally woke up and came over. They didn't know what to make of the scene–a tiny handicapper with scraped knees and a large red rubber ball was standing over a large 'normal' kid, who had a rapidly growing fat lip. Apparently they did the wise thing–they simply assumed that two kids got in a scuffle in the playground and that it was not that big a deal. My dad says that today, the police would have been called, we both would have been arrested, and there would have been lawsuits for years. I think that's a bit of an exaggeration, but it adds flavor to the story.

Apparently, it was a big enough problem that they called our house to warn my parents that I had two scraped knees and had been in a fight, but my dad was at work, and my mom was at school. Then my teacher called again later that night–I guess they were a little worried. They really needn't have bothered. When my mom met my bus at the end of the day, she noticed my knees, asked if I was OK, and when I said yes she showed no particular interest, because they really didn't hurt very much, I'd had a lot worse already as a kid falling down all over the place. I am sure she figured I just fell down while playing, which was sort of true. The whole thing could have stopped there, but it would have denied my father supreme pleasure. Because when the teacher called that night, my dad answered the phone and listened to the story of the fight, at least as much as the teachers saw, and I don't know what the hell they saw. According to my dad and mom, the conversation went sort of like this:

Teacher: "I was calling about Shane's scraped knees and to explain that he was seen by the school nurse and they were cleaned and bandaged, but he kept taking the band aids off. He wouldn't keep them on. But he seems OK. It happened during recess. He got in a small fight with another child, but everything seems OK. He was checked out thoroughly by the nurse. I just wanted you to know how it happened." She was very apologetic or so say my parents.

My dad: "Oh yeah. We saw them and he said he got them on the playground. These things happen. He seems just fine. I imagined he just fell down running or something. But I appreciate your calling us. I'm sorry to hear he got in a fight with one of his classmates."

Teacher: "Well, it wasn't exactly one of his classmates. It was general recess and it was a fight with one of the kids NOT in special ed."

My dad (seemingly more concerned): "Can you tell me what happened?"

Teacher: "Not really much to tell. One of the teacher's aides saw the whole thing. The other child took Shane's ball away from him, pushed him to the ground, and Shane got up and punched him in the face and took it back."

My Dad: "So what exactly happened to the other kid?"

Teacher: "Well, he sure looks a lot worse than Shane. Big fat lip, but nothing permanent. The nurse checked him out and his teeth are fine. And he is getting a lot of grief from his friends for getting beat up by such a little guy like Shane, which I must admit is a little odd. We were all so shocked that Shane hit him–Shane is such a friendly easygoing child. It was sort of a unique situation for all of us. It's never happened before. But there is no question that the other child pushed Shane first after taking his ball and that's how his knees got scraped."

My dad (now beaming): "Well that's too bad. I'm glad the other child is OK, though I'm sorry he has a swollen lip. We will definitely speak to Shane about this. We'll talk to him about not fighting."

Teacher: "I appreciate your understanding and am glad Shane is feeling well."

Yeah, yeah–they talked another minute or so and then my dad hung up. He turned to me and asked if I punched a kid who took my ball. I simply said yes. You'd think I won the heavyweight championship of the world. We started high-fiving and he picked me up and threw me in the air a couple of times, just as happy as he could be. He said he was very proud of me. Then he got serious again and said, "But remember, no fighting unless someone hits you first. Right?" I nodded in agreement. Then some more shows of victory until my mom finally told him to stop, that it might confuse me, and she didn't want me to be a fighter. We calmed down, but he was smiling that same grin the whole damn night.

Since I already mentioned it, I had one almost identical retake of this incident on a school playground during recess in Philly about 10 years later. 'Normal' kid comes up to me on the playground and simply grabs my ball from me and says "fuck-off retard". Similar situation except we were all older and I was one of about 20 white kids in an all-black school. But no racial overtones since I had already made my conversion to being a black person long before, so he was one of my 'brothers'–just not one I got along with very well. Well, my photographic memory kicked in and I immediately flashed back to the SF incident. I instinctively realized I didn't want to engage in an argument or get shoved to the ground. Too late, he knocked me down during my flashback. But I got up fast and smashed him in the mouth and took my ball back. Same phone call that night from the teacher with apologies made. Same celebration from my dad. He called it 'déjà-vu'. I have no clue about that word and can't say it, but I think he meant it was just like in SF when I hit the first kid. And I never got into a fistfight with anyone else ever again my whole life.

Chapter 3
How I became a sports star and hung with babes

So I was set in school, I liked it, and went there for the full three years we lived in SF. I won't bore you with endless elementary school stories, mostly because, once again, I can't remember many particularly interesting ones except my fistfight. Which tells you it was a pretty mellow time. But my parents liked it, I liked it, my teachers liked me and treated me really well. All the kids were cool, too. Though the kid I socked in the mouth never talked to me again–he kept his distance. So enough of that, unless something interesting pops into my head.

After school, I went to this incredibly cool place called 'Challenge to Learning', which was a big residential house that had a group of handicappers like me. Now THAT was a special place. First off, my parents and I thought it was pretty amazing that SF not only had great special ed in schools, but they had after school programs for special ed. We later learned that it was one of the only afterschool programs for special ed in the city and there were only like 20 kids in it, but you get my point.

Next, the teachers were freaks and hippies that looked

like my dad a bit, but they were cooler. And you know what their job was? To have fun with us and make sure we learned stuff while we were having fun! We did games and little classes in that big house that seemed a lot more like a house than a school. Real school type stuff, though. But a lot of the time, we cruised around the neighborhood, doing 'life skills'. Like riding the bus, or going to eat in a restaurant and behaving ourselves properly, and stuff like that. I was already a pro at eating out, but I was quite surprised that a lot of the other kids didn't seem so good at it. On the other hand, I had seldom ridden on a public bus and always with my parents and the whole ticket thing and knowing which bus to take, and the bus numbers, and when to get off, and changing buses, phew!; that sort of stuff was hard for me. So you see, everyone gets good at some things, but not so good at others and that's why you always have to keep learning stuff. Your whole life. That's a little piece of 'wisdom' from me, even though I don't know what wisdom is, as you will later find out. Or as I commonly say to this day: "Watch and learn". I don't know if I made that up or I heard it somewhere. But my parents and anyone around me just crack up whenever I say it.

Riding the bus was almost as cool as where we went. We went to McDonalds or something like that to learn how to order food and pay and carry trays to our seats, and clean up before we left. We went to laundromats to learn how to wash clothes and put coins in the machines, and add soap and stuff. I didn't care that much for that, but I really loved Tuesdays. Bowling! Yup, every Tuesday we went on the bus to go bowling and man, I got pretty good. I was rolling way above a hundred. And get this. I didn't know that I had a special skill that no one else had. If you bowled according to my rules, no one could beat me, not even the freaky teachers. See, I have this thing about bowling balls. My dad says I am sometimes neurotic (no clue what that means) and my mom says I am just very cautious, but it is generally agreed that I have a unique bowling style. The fact of the matter is that I am scared shitless to put my fingers into those three holes in the bowling ball. I am absolutely convinced that one or more of my fingers will get stuck when I throw the ball and one of those fingers will come off my hand and go all the way down the lane INSIDE the ball. Accordingly, I used two hands and rocked the ball between my legs until I was ready to let go and throw it down the lane. Nowadays, I use the lightest ball I can find, curl my hand and wrist to hold the ball in one hand (which is not easy given my small hands) and slowly roll the ball down the lane, with a fairly respectable skill level. Later, when I got my own personal bowling ball in Tucson, the guy at the bowling alley couldn't believe it when my parents bought me all new bowling gear and a shiny, light, golden bowling ball and told him there was no need to fit me for finger holes–that there would be no finger holes. He laughed at first, but then went out and watched me bowl a 170 my way, shook his head, and did as he was told.

So my weekdays were pretty busy. Off to school around 8:30, then Challenge to Learning after school till about 5 pm. Free school buses from home to school, school to Challenge, and a van back home at the end of the day. I am told they don't do all that stuff for free anymore. That's kinda sad, don't you think? Anyway, I was sort of pooped at the end of the day, but a good tired. But a short nap and dinner always brought me back to life for nighttime fun and games and TV with the parents. More on that later. My parents are very strange people.

You would think that was enough for a little guy like me, but you would be wrong. Because on Saturdays, I went to the Recreation Center, otherwise known as the Rec Center. We wouldn't have known about it at all, except the wife of one of my dad's fellow residents (his name was Darryl–

solid guy) told us about it. Her name was Jackie (really nice woman) and she was sort of a special ed honcho in SF and knew everyone there and sometimes I would see her stop in and she would play with me a while. Now the folks who ran that place weren't hippies or freaks, but they were really into sports. I think that's why it was called the rec center. It was a building either in or right next to the San Francisco Zoo, because we got to see the animals all the time just by stepping out the door. Talk about cool–I love zoos.

. Now these teachers weren't really teachers–they were more like coaches and taught us all different sports like volleyball, basketball, softball, track, swimming (yup, we would go to a pool where I could show off), soccer, war, dancing (yeah, I know that's not a sport, but it's cool and they have coaches), and gymnastics. I left gymnastics last for emphasis, because that was my claim to everlasting fame.

I had the two greatest gymnastic coaches that ever lived. I couldn't pronounce their names properly and since my parents hardly ever went to the rec center again after checking it out one time and giving it a seal of approval, I am embarrassed to say I can't put their names in this memoir. I am ashamed for two reasons. First and least important, they made me a great gymnast for my age and devoted a large part of their time with me. Second and more importantly, these were the hottest and most beautiful women I had ever had the pleasure of knowing well. And they were so affectionate!! Hugs and kisses for everything I did. They thought I was the cutest guy in the world. I'm still a bachelor and intend to stay that way, but had I ever gotten married, it would have been with one of those incredible women. I hope if they ever read this book, they contact me, because I would love to see them again. Damn I wish I had their phone numbers.

So my big sport was gymnastics when I was that age and I did everything–parallel bars, horse, tumbling, high bar–you name it, I did it. I was a spinning top, or as my dad later said, a whirling dervish. And given my coaches, I was more than motivated to impress. I just love hugging hot babes and man, would they hug me when I did things right in gymnastics. I was their prodigy, whatever that is. Now I'm a little short, which worked out great; when they hugged me, they shoved my face between their breasts, which is a really cool feeling. This became a lifelong lesson in itself. My dad just cracks up when I wink at him during these moments nowadays, but never says anything. My mom just laughs quietly. I pretty much love all women–women are just so much fun to hang with. I learned several important lessons very early, on how to endear myself to women. Some of it is sheer luck–I have big blue eyes with white crystals, I'm pretty funny (if I do say so myself), and I can make almost anyone laugh when I want to. And I'm in pretty good shape, though that is starting to fade as I enter middle age. But you gotta have strategies. The first is to just be yourself, especially if you are funny, and I am that. But you're born with that just like you're born with Down syndrome. I got lucky. But as they say, luck can carry you only so far.

I first discovered the "tattoo" strategy by accident. A beautiful waitress at a restaurant had these great roses tattooed around her belly button and she wore a short t-shirt so you could see them a little. I was transfixed. So after she came back with our drinks, I asked to see them better and she lifted up her t-shirt a bit. They were really cool, but back then I didn't really understand what they were. So I asked if I could touch them and she smiled and said sure. So I gently rubbed her belly and MAN, DID THAT FEEL GREAT. She laughed and said it tickled but let me rub her tummy for quite a bit–she thought I was cute and later, my dad said it was because I was "non-threatening". I still don't really understand what that means, and I still don't understand why my dad later said: "If I tried to do that, I would be in jail." She thought I was so cute, she brought over some more waitresses with tattoos and I got to rub, caress and touch a whole bunch of pretty girls right there in the restaurant. I may be handicapped, but let me tell you something you should remember for life if you're a guy: If a girl has a tattoo showing, she is proud of it, she wants it to be seen, and if you're the right person at the right time, you likely can rub it. This is one of my key social strategies with women. To this very day.

I have other social strategies, however I can't give away all my secrets. But here's another tidbit. When I meet a girl, I immediately ask: "Remember me?" This works two ways. If we've met before, like at a restaurant where we go a lot, then she gushes all over that I remember her and that's when the hugs and maybe a kiss on the cheek come in. But if we've never met, they usually look a little uncomfortable, cause they think they may have forgotten meeting a guy with a 'handicap' and according to my dad, that's politically incorrect, whatever that means. So those girls are even friendlier than the ones who already know me, cause they go out of their way to be nice. I gotta tell you, most people are really good people, even if you do have to sometimes push them a bit.

Sorry for the digression–I'm not a professional writer. I forgot to tell you about my gymnastics career. It was short, only a couple of years, but I won 5 gold medals at the California State Special Olympics in LA when I was 8 eight years old, the youngest age group they allowed. I know, that's pretty impressive, but I must say, it helped that all along the path to greatness, I was aided by the fact that the overwhelming majority of 8 year old special athletes were scared shitless to jump on the equipment and flip around all over the place. My dad had been flipping me around and bouncing me off couches and pillows and his shoulders for fun for so many years that it was natural for me. He says today he would be in prison for child abuse, but boy, we had fun. I loved that stuff. So I practiced with my coaches every Saturday at the rec center and got real good for a little twerp. But I never told my parents 'cause I didn't want them interfering with the hugging situation–I thought it was unique to have two gorgeous coaches, and I was right. Never happened again. The Special Olympics needs to work on that from what I see on TV. Anyway, I won a whole bunch of district titles and made it to the San Francisco finals. That's when I got the bad news. They had to tell my parents to get permission for me to go, since it wasn't part of the Saturday programs. They called my dad one night, a couple of days before the meet. The conversation went something like this, as I was later told:

"Hello. Is this Shane's dad? My name is Carol (I had to pick a random name), and I am one of Shane's gymnastics coaches and we wanted to make sure you were bringing him to the SF finals on Thursday night. We hadn't heard back from you with the forms and I know he and we are excited about it."

My father got a funny look. "I think you have the wrong number, but the right first name. My son doesn't do gymnastics. He's handicapped."

"No, we have the right number, I'm sure. Jane (another fake name–damn I wish I could remember better) says she met your wife and Shane has been coming to the rec center for almost 2 years now, working hard on his routines. He's really good–we think he will win and get to go to the state level."

"Well, that does sound a little familiar–the rec center that is, but I think as his father, I would know if he was a gymnast, especially a good one. I really think you are confusing him with someone else."

So these are my caring parents. They checked out the

rec center for me to go there every Saturday and thought it was a good fit for me. I thought it was fantastic. But once they put me on the bus every Saturday morning, I could have been in China for all they cared. Unbeknownst to me, they would go for brunch, drink a bunch of alcohol, party around all day, eat, see friends, and then rush home to meet me at 5 o'clock when the bus returned, with this happy but concerned look as if they had been waiting by the phone to hear of some emergency about me. At least that's what I thought. Had I known what they were doing, I would have stayed with them all day. I mean gymnastics and play is fun, but I think they were having the better time. Whatever.

The bottom line is that my parents had no clue that I was a blossoming gymnastics star, of sorts. They came to the SF Finals where I kicked ass and won 5 events to get me to the State Finals. They had incredulous looks on their faces and I could tell that my mom thought I was going to get killed on the parallel bars, but they seemed happy enough and slapped me on the back so much that it turned red. Then we went home and they drank a bunch of wine to celebrate my excellence, a fact that they were completely ignorant about only a few days before. They were probably congratulating themselves on their fine parenting.

So off we went to Los Angeles for the California State Special Olympics the next month. We're talking early 1980's here. Fortunately, the team flew on its own–no parents allowed on the plane or in the hotel. We had an ITINERARY. We wore uniforms, blazers with insignias–we were studs, very professional. This didn't seem to bother my parents who I am sure were drinking and partying on another plane and some other hotel anyway. We crossed paths a few times in LA, but fortunately not too often.

I won't bore you with many details, other than to point out I collected 5 gold medals (did I mention that before?) in gymnastics. I deserved 4 of them. But not in the floor exercises. I really sucked in that cause I started doing somersaults (well, forwards rolls, actually) and lost track of things and just rolled around the mat for about 2 minutes like a top until I was so dizzy I couldn't stand up. I forgot the cartwheels, handsprings, headstands, backward rolls – pretty much everything else. Finally, I stood up and threw my hands up in the air to show that I was done and noticed that the judges were all smiling those insanely large grins that I was able to command at that age, due to my huge blue eyes that were too big for my head, my blond hair and my size, which was that of about a 4 year old. I was what was called 'adorable' in those days, though I am no slouch even now. Remember the Perry Como commercial for the Florida United Way, so believe me when I say I was adorable. Fact is fact.

I had already learned that when adults grin like that and especially when they get a couple of happy tears, that's your shot. So I ran over to the judges' table and kissed each and every one of them on the cheek, including the two guys. Yeah, then came all the hugs and what not–bottom line–I got the gold in the floor exercises, too. You do whatever it takes to win.

The other bizarre thing about my performance occurred right at the end of my routine on the parallel bars. One of my last big moves was to do a backward roll, and then a forward roll right into a shoulder stand with my feet straight up in the air. It was hard to learn and hard to do every time. Sometimes I would fall to the side or just go too far over. That's why they have spotters all over the place. But my coaches got me pretty well prepped and I was confident. What I didn't realize was that there would be around 3,000 people watching me do it–this was at Pauley Pavilion, a famous arena where UCLA plays basketball I think. But it wasn't that I was nervous. It was that the people got me excited. So I did my rolls perfectly and went right into the shoulder stand and held it for like 5 or 10 seconds like I was taught. But then all of a sudden the whole place went nuts and they started cheering and screaming like maniacs. I'm talking several thousand people. Suddenly, I got so juiced up that I accidentally 'pressed' myself into a handstand. I had no idea what I was doing, but the place went even more nuts and I did, too. I stayed up there as long as I could and when I finally dismounted, I got a standing ovation. My coaches and parents had their mouths open. I didn't even know what a handstand was and I had never even been shown how to do that once in my entire life. It just sort of happened. People were coming up to me for an hour to shake my hand. Strangely, I tried to do it again many times in practice for months and I was never able to do it again. It was a once in a lifetime thing, but it came at the perfect time.

The other memorable thing about those Special Olympics was meeting celebrities. I mean there were supposed to be a ton of them, but I didn't see that many, I wasn't much of a movie guy back then. At the closing ceremonies, there were all these people signing autographs and having their pictures taken with special athletes, but I think most of them were fakes. Real phonies. To be sure, Meadowlark Lemon of the Harlem Globetrotters was there and he was really cool with me and carried me around on his shoulders–we hung for at least 15 minutes. I bet you readers don't even know who he was cause you're intellectuals (at least that's what my dad says), but I recognized him in his t-shirt and shorts. And some other celebs from sports. But then my parents appeared, dragging some wise ass along with them for me to meet. They had the nerve to tell me it was the Fonz, my favorite character from TV–yeah I'm sure you never heard of him either, but he was big in his time. So I'm looking at this little guy in slacks, loafers, and a dress shirt–this is supposed to be a tough motorcycle guy with really slick hair, and he looks like my parents' accountant. So I told him to buzz off, I had other people to meet. Well, he laughed but wouldn't leave me alone. He went off and got a t-shirt, wet his hair down and did endless imitations of the "real" Fonz that were pathetic. And I told him so. My parents started laughing and then this guy started laughing, and I didn't know what to do, so I turned, bent over and farted at him and went off. I use this maneuver occasionally since it allows me to leave a situation with people laughing. I looked back and felt bad cause the guy seemed to be laughing so hard that he was crying, and I hate when people cry.

Life returned to normal pretty quickly after those Olympics, but a week later my parents said we were going to march in a parade. I might have been a fool then, but now I know it wasn't a parade, it was a march. A protest. A march against people who did not want to spend any money to educate Mongols and people like me. Well, screw them, I was off to march and it was a blast. Once again, tons of people including a fair share of babes who all wanted to give me a hug and put me on their shoulders. What a great way to spend a sunny afternoon. Later my parents said we won. Maybe we did, maybe we didn't, but I never saw any medals or ribbons.

Chapter 4
My life as an artist and my good friend Jerry

I was pretty well set for my education and recreation in SF. And then my mom started up college again, only it wasn't a gigantic university like in Minnesota. It was called the San Francisco Art Institute. It was small but beautiful with a fantastic view of the whole San Francisco Bay area from the rooftop cafe. It didn't have a basketball team or football team, but that was OK with me. I used to go there a lot when I didn't have school like on holidays, Christmas break, spring break and that sort of stuff and on weekends and even at night. Because when you study to be an artist, you work on your stuff all the time. We would go in at night to the sculpture area and I would get me a big hunk of clay and mash it around endlessly. And sometimes I would go into the dark room with my mom to make photographs, which I love. I forgot to mention that we always had a darkroom in our house until we finally moved to Tucson many years later. By that time, we all had digital cameras and I'll tell you about my photographs some other time. I specialize in sunsets, women and public bathrooms. I think my dad was pissed off at himself for painting one of our bathrooms completely black in Minnesota, so he could have a darkroom. Apparently that wasn't appealing to other people who didn't want a black bathroom or bathtub. There was some problem about that when we left and I didn't really understand it. Somebody got that place with the black bathroom though and I guess it was OK with them. But my dad never did that ever again.

My favorite things at the Art Institute were just like my mom's favorites, painting and drawing. And I got all sorts of great materials to work with–and was able to get most of it all over myself most of the time, which was almost as much fun as painting. I just loved smearing charcoal all over myself as well.

I even got to hang out in classes on painting and drawing because the teachers there were very laid back and let me be a little student. Sometimes I got my own place at a table or a thing called an easel. I can't remember all their names but there was one guy in particular who became a great friend to all of us–Julius Hatofsky. My mom and dad think he was one of the greatest painters of the 20th century–that's when the years started with the number 19. Now they start with 20. We all thought he was one of the greatest people we ever met. And so did a lot of other people. None of his friends called him Julius though, he was called Jerry–I have no idea why. I loved his classes especially, because in the drawing class, THERE WERE NAKED WOMEN!!! That's right, they would put naked women right in the center of the room on a little platform with a bunch of stuff around them and everyone tried to draw what they saw. Some of the people saw things very different from what I saw, but I didn't focus much on my drawing on those days. I pretty much studied up on naked women. Now here's something strange that I never understood. A lot of the times they had naked men in the center of the room. And sometimes, old men or women. And fat and skinny people too. That had much less interest for me. But I would go up to all of them when I could and say hello and they were all very nice to me. No one ever asked me to go up there naked, but no way would I have taken all my clothes off in front of everyone. I'm not shy, but the whole thing was sort of weird. But a good weird.

Now Jerry was the calmest and gentlest man I ever met. I believe he was either a hypnotist (I saw them in Vegas later and occasionally on TV) or we had something my dad calls 'mental telepathy'. That's when you can talk to someone without actually talking. You just know what the other person is saying or thinking without having to use words. I never had that feeling before or after meeting Jerry. It wasn't like we were best friends, though we certainly were good friends. But we didn't speak a lot for two reasons. First, Jerry couldn't really understand my speech very well. Second, Jerry was a very quiet and shy guy who hardly ever talked, at least not until he had a couple of drinks, which is when he would open up and tell cool stories, like when he was a policeman in NYC for a year, or when he was a parachute guy in World War II (I love those movies). But Jerry loved to walk everywhere. And very slowly, because he was always looking around at everything, from bugs on the sidewalk, to clouds in the sky, to shadows of buildings. Which helped me a lot, since I am a slow walker as well. Here's an absolute fact: Jerry never learned to drive a car. Like me, except he did that on purpose. He said if you drove a car you missed just about everything interesting there is to see in the world–he told that to my mom and dad who told it to me. I think this is called 'philosophy' and frankly, given my dislike of walking, I'm glad to get rides everywhere. Except when I was with Jerry. But I think I understand it a little now, especially after I moved to the desert in Tucson, where you do miss a lot of stuff if you are not walking. Of course, I still prefer riding.

So the first time I was in Jerry's drawing class with my mom, he strolled over to her spot and took a look at me sitting on the floor of the studio next to her, scribbling my heart out with charcoal on a big piece of paper. Somehow a lot of it was getting into my mouth, which tasted awful. He smiled down at me with the kindest eyes I have ever seen and I smiled back. We said nothing. Then he walked on to look at other students drawing. After about an hour of this, I worked up quite a thirst and asked my mom if we could go get some milk at the rooftop cafe. Mostly to get the taste of the charcoal out of my mouth. She said to wait a few minutes and then we'd go get some milk. Well, Jerry was standing near us and heard it. He walked over and looked down at me and for some inexplicable reason, I put my hand out for him. Now let me say right up front, I have never been a hand-holding guy in my life. My parents yelled at me all the time to grab their hands just to cross the street and not get hit by a car. And Jerry wasn't a pick you up on his shoulders and huggy sort of guy either. But he gently took hold of my hand and got me on my feet and we walked out of the studio to go get some milk. He stopped a couple of times before we left to say something to a student here and there and then we went to the rooftop cafe. We hardly spoke as we walked and I was so mellow and relaxed, I thought I was going to fall asleep standing. When we got to the cafe, he showed me two small milk cartons, one chocolate and one regular, and I pointed to the regular. He got a coffee and we took our drinks outside to the wall overlooking San Francisco Bay. We were there a good ten minutes, just looking all around, and now I think I was hypnotized. Jerry would point to a big ship or one of the islands in the bay or one of the bridges and just say something like, "Look at that, Shane" or "Isn't the sky really blue today", you know, stuff I could understand. And I would look and get fixed to that spot and stare for quite awhile. This became a routine for virtually every class of his I ever went to. We would just hold hands and walk to the cafe or sometimes to the fishpond in the courtyard entrance of the school, where there were big goldfish. Sometimes, Jerry would have breadcrumbs and he'd put a few in one spot to make the fish come right up to me. Once, he gave me a handful and I just threw them in all at once like a fool, scattered in the wind. But no fish came up to me. Jerry then showed me his handful and how he took just a tiny amount and gently put them on the water right next to us and then the fish would come right up to me. Never said a word, just showed me, and that's how I did it from then on and it worked for me too.

After a while, we became pretty good friends with Jerry and his wife, Linda, and would sometimes go to his house, which wasn't a house at all. It was pretty much a factory (my mom said it was a warehouse, but I don't know that word) with all sorts of machines he used to make really cool wood tables with pictures on them made from wood–and I might add, the coolest wooden toilet seat I have ever seen or sat on in my life. That was his hobby (that's what he called it), when he wasn't painting, but my parents say he was a great artist at that too. Now this factory was HUGE. The ceilings were like 50 fifty feet high and it was unlike any house I have ever seen before or since. He built a bed you had to climb a ladder to get into, and I loved going up and down that thing. The whole place was filled with paintings and drawings, most of them bigger than cars. I don't know what they meant or were saying, since I had already learned that people liked to talk about what a picture is saying to them–I don't really get that whole thing–but the colors of his paintings were really beautiful, and I think he is my favorite painter too. And I've seen a shitload of paintings in person and in art books over my life. And it wasn't just the ceilings that were huge. The windows were huge, the whole place was pretty much one immense room like an airplane hangar (I never knew that word before), but Jerry put up a few walls to separate some areas into rooms, like where the machines were, and the bathroom, and a room for Linda. It was the coolest house I ever saw, except maybe the big building where we lived in Philly, but I'll get to that later.

Jerry used to have occasional parties at his place and they were a blast. I think everyone really liked him because he had hundreds of friends come to his parties–all his students, old and new, lots of artists, and some of the models and lots of people I haven't a clue about. But everyone ate and drank like crazy and they were great parties for me. When I got tired, I would crawl up into his bed, which was off to the side, but still inside the party, so I could look down and watch everyone.

And man, could he cook. Dinner at his place was like going to a restaurant. And he would make special stuff so I could eat, since he quickly learned I was a finicky eater. Sometimes we'd have dinner at our house, and my mom would make Cuban food or maybe we'd barbecue. But no matter what, when we'd finish, we always took a walk after dinner. A long, slow walk, with me holding Jerry's hand and him pointing out a few things here and there for me to look at. Most often without ever saying a word.

Oh yeah, back to the models for a minute. Once Jerry and I became friends, and after I watched him place the models in different positions for the students to draw (this is called posing for those who don't understand art), I took it upon myself to help him by walking up to the models quite often and asking them to change their pose. The first few times they would look at Jerry and he would just smile and nod, and then they would get into whatever position I asked. Now I don't really know squat about art posing, but I do know interesting positions. Part of this is because when you have Down syndrome, you are really very flexible–it's part of the condition as I have been told, though I didn't need anyone to tell me that I could twist myself into all sorts of positions that no one else could. For the first 15 or 20 years of my life, I watched TV on the floor with my legs stretched out at what my dad says is 180 degrees and my elbows on the floor in front of me, with my head in my hands, which apparently is difficult for most people. Felt very comfortable to me. Or other times, I would relax by putting both my feet behind my head and when my dad walked by, he would spin me like a top, which was really fun.

So I would try to get these models (at least all the young, pretty girls) into really cool positions with their legs over their heads or doing splits, but usually they either couldn't do it or couldn't hold it for very long. They'd never make it in gymnastics at the Special Olympics. And for old people and fat people I always placed them bent over holding onto their ankles in some way. The only time I ever heard Jerry burst out in a real loud laugh in class was the day he asked me why I did that. I walked over to a bent over older, female model and pointed to all the skin, fat and breasts hanging down and said, "Isn't that funny looking?" He was definitely crying while laughing and I knew I had told a good joke.

We kept in touch with Jerry even after we moved to Philly and he came out to visit us a couple of times because he had a war friend who lived in Camden as well. We visited him and Linda a few times in SF, too. And we'd call sometimes just to say hello. I can't explain it, but he and I had a very special friendship that my parents call a 'bond'. They say it doesn't happen often, but we just had this thing between us. Jerry died a while back because he was much older than my parents and I'm not supposed to know, but I do. My parents never tell me when people die, but I watch a lot of TV and movies and I know about people dying. I just don't know where they go after they die. I have several friends and people I liked a lot who I suddenly stopped hearing from for a long time. And I'm pretty sure they're dead, but my parents won't talk about it. It makes me sad too, so I don't talk about it either.

Chapter 5
The Bar Life

OK, now on to the nightlife. My parents went out on their own enough, but lots of times I went along and I became quite familiar with the hotspots of SF in those days. For us, a lot of it centered around the intersection of Columbus and Broadway (yeah, I don't know those names but I sure as hell know the areas). It was the center point around which you could go to North Beach cafes, Chinatown eats, great bars and fine strip clubs. Not that my parents would take me or go to strip clubs, but I figured a way around that. You see, one of our favorite bars was a place called Spec's, which my dad says is still open today, though he isn't sure if Spec is still there. He was the owner and a solid guy. It was a really fine bar in those days with the coolest thing I had ever seen before in a bar. It had signs on the ceiling–I thought that was hysterical. I can read most signs if they are simple enough and most of these were. But my favorite one had to be translated to me by my parents. It said, "Please do not urinate on the floor". Which was explained to me as "Please don't pee on the floor". That just cracked me up. Anyway, when you wanted to go to the bathroom at Spec's in those days, you had to go up a really tall set of stairs. So the first time we went there, I was off to the bathroom because I always have to pee when I drink anything. And when I got to the top of the stairs, I started hearing loud music and saw sorta red lights blinking, going down a short hallway. And then standing in that hallway, were really hot women smoking cigarettes and wearing robes that were half open with either no clothes on or just a few small pieces. My god, you could even see through some of the robes. Seems that the bathroom was shared with a building that had its front all the way around the block (on Broadway says my mom and dad). Spec's shared the bathroom with a strip club, the stores that had pictures of naked college coeds right in front!! So every time I went to the bathroom, I had a pretty good chance of seeing cool strippers partly undressed. And they were nice to me too, cause they liked my whole adorable thing as much as anyone. I tried to go down the steps and take a look at the show a couple of times, but there was always a guy there to stop you from getting in. But a few times they let me take a peek, and to this day, I regret I never got to go to one of those shows–it looked pretty awesome. Let's just say I had to a pee an awful lot when we went to Spec's. My mom and dad didn't really care because they were incompetent parents and my mom certainly didn't care since she knew I was getting used to seeing naked girls at her art school. So the bar scene served me well.

There were other good bars around there that were starting to get a little touristy (so say my parents), but we all liked going to Vesuvio's in the afternoons when it was empty, to drink and play backgammon, which I started to get good at. I've lost my touch these days, but I am still a kick ass dominoes player from my Miami days.

In nearby North Beach, we almost always hung out at the Savoy, a fine cafe, which was a great place with lots of crazy but good people and some music too. No matter where you sat outside at the Savoy, you ended up getting in conversations with the people next to you, and it was fun, because they were all hippie freaks and everyone loved to argue in a nice way about anything you said. Sometimes, it almost ended up in a fistfight, but not really, just a lot of showboating. Not my parents, they were mellow and never argued with anyone, but we all loved the scene. People were cool. It was on a side street with some other cafes that we went to. But most of them are gone now, or so say my parents. And Chinatown has changed a lot, though it still has the best dim sum place we ever went to called the Hang Ah, which is in a little basement. The ladies there really took care of me and I always got the freshest steamed pork buns you could get.

I know this is starting to sound like a tourist travel news report, but I thought it was important for the flow of my story that you knew of the places I went to in SF. I mean I had a real social life there and got around big time. And not just SF. We went to Berkeley and Oakland to hang out as well. Best breakfast East Bay: Mama's Royal Cafe. Best Irish coffees in a cafeteria East Bay: Brennan's.

But our eventual home base bar after we moved from the Marina to be closer to the hospital my dad worked at (UCSF) was a great Irish bar, The Little Shamrock. That's where I learned to like Guinness, sippin' on my dad's, only to lose my taste for it years later. How sad. My dad never lost his taste for it. It was real homey, very old, people treated me no different than anyone else—no special hugs or affection, just another Joe coming in for his drink and I liked that a lot. They treated me like a real man even though I was just a little kid. They had tables with chess and backgammon and we'd sit the night away just chillin' whenever we could. We just looked them up on my computer and saw they are still open but my dad was pissed that they had TV's on the wall now. He hates TV's in bars, but he's an old fart, and just doesn't understand the importance of TV entertainment. We argue about this quite often, but just joking because he knows I am never going to stop watching. We all have our favorite hangouts in Tucson now, and you can bet your ass my favorite ones have big TV's and his don't.

OK, this isn't really a very important subject, so let's move on. My dad simply asked about some of my favorite places for the book and I told him. Enough said.

Chapter 6
Food fights are not only for the immature

Life in SF was the fast lane for me and I hope you've gotten a taste of the life I was able to enjoy there, cruising the Streets of SF (that was a TV show by the way), at a very young age. But like anyplace, your home is where everything really important happens, and we had a grand time there.

It's very important that you realize how incredibly immature my parents were, have been and still are. They simply have the minds of children and since I also have the mind of a child, we live a child-like existence, which is pretty neat.

Regarding our home life, the single most important fact was that we hardly ever had it to ourselves. You see, in those days, SF was a great place to visit (still is, I guess), and almost everyone my parents had ever known ended up visiting and staying with us for weeks and on some occasions, months. I'm talking people from Boston, NYC, Minneapolis, Miami, Ohio, and even Wales–that's in a place called Europe. We even had relatives from Argentina come visit us, and we didn't even know we had relatives from that country. My parents worked it out on a calendar and it turns out we had visitors living in one of our two small apartments (the Marina apartment and later, an apartment in the Inner Sunset) for 8 months a year over three years. Most people wouldn't have put up with it and had my mom not been there, I think my dad would have thrown most of them out, but we persevered (pretentious word). But ignoring our general lack of privacy, and given that most of our visitors were as immature as my parents, it turned out to be fun, with the exception that I almost spent 8 months a year arguing with someone over what we would watch on the single TV in our house. Without visitors, I pretty much had control of the TV. My parents weren't that interested. Oh, they watched TV sometimes. It just wasn't that big a deal to them, which it was to me and within vague limits, we would watch whatever I picked. Visitors always wanted to pick their own shows. They didn't realize it was my turf. For the first few visitors, my parents would work on me to compromise (that means give in sometimes). But after a few months of that shit, and specifically after I pointed out that these people were getting free room and board, they simply informed anyone who came to stay that they had zero say on the TV. It was declared my TV as a first notice to anyone who came to stay. And I will be grateful to them for that decision for the rest of my life.

How immature were/are my parents? Well, let's get into it right now. For starters, we had frequent food fights. I'm talking people who were on the verge of becoming a real doctor and an artist. Yup, if someone said something making fun of the other at the dinner table, a common response was to simply throw food at them. I was carefully kept out of this behavior as a participant, but being a close observer, it was only a matter of time before I sank to their level. My first involvement occurred during a spaghetti dinner. My dad makes a pretty decent red sauce. I don't remember exactly what was said, and in this particular case, no food was initially thrown. I think he said that someone at work called my mom a stupid cow and he said he defended her by saying she wasn't a cow. Just something to be a wise ass. My mom smiled and got up with her plate as if she was taking it into the kitchen, but it was still half full. I was studying this very closely you see. As she passed by his chair, she turned and dumped all her spaghetti on his head and without saying a word, returned to her chair. My dad remained calm and showed no emotion except a little smile. He then got up with his plate and walked over to my mom, grabbed a big handful of spaghetti and shoved it down the front of her shirt, and then returned to his seat. I knew right away that they WANTED to have a food fight because neither of them tried to duck or stop the other one from dumping the spaghetti. No one said anything for about a minute and they started to giggle a little. Then they started to laugh the laugh that you can't stop. You know, the one when you start laughing and if you even look at the other person, you burst out laughing. I get that all the time, my whole life. I finally decided that I had been left out for way too long and announced, "watch me", and proceeded to take my own plate of spaghetti and turned it upside down and dumped it on my own head.

Well, that set up probably the largest food fight we ever had. I think they always previously left me out so as not to piss me off or offend me. But I wanted in and now it came true. Spaghetti was flying everywhere, sauce and all. Italian bread, salad (with oil/vinegar), olives, cheese bits, and a few glasses of drinks—mostly my coke and some water—they were too cheap to waste the beer or wine or whatever they were drinking. I don't think any more details are necessary, you get the picture. We all ended up on the floor in a heap, just doing the crying laughter thing and occasionally smearing some food on each other. Hey, they were young and frisky then, and so was I. Unfortunately, I also learned that night, that cleaning up after a food fight is a real pain in the ass. You gotta wash the floor, the walls, the furniture, everything–and you still can't get all the stains out. They didn't seem to care and that night when we all went to sleep (well, I went to sleep earlier), it was a pretty happy night for absolutely nothing of interest happening except throwing some food around. Amazing how you can create fun out of nothing. I always try to remember that.

As an aside, we had smaller food fights amongst ourselves, food fights that consisted of perhaps some bread being thrown, water fights, and even had food fights occasionally when guests came over. I remember one night this really straight looking well-dressed guy came over wearing a tie and jacket. My dad couldn't believe it and I heard him making fun of the guy in the kitchen to my mom. He said, "Why the hell did he wear a tie and jacket? Does he think we do that sort of stuff at home? I mean I invited him for dinner cause he lives alone and I thought he might like to get out since he's sort of shy." My mom just told my dad to be quiet and be nice. But I knew exactly what was going to happen. Every time the guy looked away, my dad kept refilling his wine glass until the guy was pretty tipsy. Actually he was pretty drunk. So they start telling a few jokes and next thing you know the guy tells some joke and my dad laughs and tosses a small piece of bread at the guy. Who then tosses some scrap of his food at my father. Yup, full bore food fight. The guy gets covered with wet rice, which turns out to be one of the worst foods for fighting since it is so sticky. And he gets too drunk to make it home to boot. So my dad cleans him up as best he can and takes him home. In the morning when we went out, there was a trail of rice on the sidewalk. And a couple of days later we got a thank you card from him for the nice dinner saying it was the best time he had since moving to SF. I think people need to have more food fights, but I never see people have them anymore. Except us, though we don't have them as often and never with guests. Being immature is a virtue says my dad–I don't get that at all (what the hell is a virtue?), but I do get food fights now, for sure.

Chapter 7
My unwholesome home life

As you can see, my claim that my parents are children is entirely true. They don't act like children–they are children. Their whole lives, even to this day. They say part of it is because of me keeping them young, but that's a pile of shit. Don't blame me for your immaturity. I could fill this whole book with the stupid things they have done in front of me their whole lives, but you'd get bored after a while. I certainly do. But in SF, they were at the height of their boorish behavior (not my choice of words), and I'll give you a couple of examples that I was in on, but not by choice.

Take the Nerf basketball incident as a perfect example of their behavior. My dad got a Nerf basketball set-up for us to shoot around the living room so we wouldn't break anything, which we had already done with real balls many times. We set it low sometimes so I could dunk, but usually it was well over my head. My parents would play on their knees. We'd play horse–that's how I learned to spell 'horse' by the way and if you don't know that game, you are not an American. Well, my mom would occasionally join in and I can't really defend her–she simply sucked. I don't mean she shot poorly. She couldn't hit the fucking backboard, let alone get the ball in the hoop. Simply pathetic. And being the kind, considerate man he is, my dad endlessly told her how much she sucked, whenever we even entered the living room and saw the basket. Well, my mom is a very hardheaded and stubborn woman. I don't know those words, but while editing this book, we discussed this word selection and my dad explained that it meant she never gives in. Since I could relate to that, the words stayed in and they fit her perfectly.

She quickly stopped playing with us. But secretly, she started practicing Nerf basketball on her own whenever my dad wasn't around. And if I was around, she told me it was a secret and to keep my mouth shut. I wasn't good at that, but she bribed me with stuff, which convinced me. And when I watched her practice, I noticed that she was only practicing one shot. A really long shot from the far corner of the living room. It was a really hard shot that I could never make. Well, she did this for about 6 months!! Probably an hour a day for 6 months, excluding days when my father was around too much to give her practice time. And by the end of those 6 months, she could hit that shot about 99% of the time. She still sort of sucked at a lot of other shots, so I didn't see the whole point of it all.

Finally, one day my mom matter-of-factly said that we should play a game of horse and listened to my dad go off on another insulting speech about her complete lameness in Nerf basketball. She listened to the whole thing and calmly said they should make a bet. He laughed and said he would bet anything. My mom said, "OK, the loser has to take off all their clothes, get up on the dining room table, and cluck like a chicken for a full minute, timed by a watch." I remember this distinctly, because I instantly thought of the models at the Art Institute, and thought that would be a great pose, but, alas, that never came to pass. But the game was on.

I was named referee, though I have no idea what a referee does in 'horse'. My mom said she was going first and my dad chuckled and told her to go ahead. She went to her spot at the far corner of the living room and banged in a bank shot. She didn't even smile, stayed very serious and intent. My father just laughed. "You think taking that ridiculous shot and making it once is going to rattle me? Prepare yourself for the table." Then he took the shot and missed badly cause it was a really hard shot. I know, because later, I tried it over and over, and I never made it once. Anyway he got an 'H'. And then my mom went back to her same spot and banged another one in. Gave a small smile. My dad shook his head and missed badly again. 'H-o'. My mom went back to her spot, but before she shot, my dad said, "You can't take the same shot over and over." I knew that was the ball game because he had officially started whining. She simply smiled and replied, "There are no rules on what shot you take." Fair enough. Well, you know the rest. My mom hit 5 straight shots, my dad never made a single one, and yes, he had to take his clothes off, get on the dining room table, and cluck like a chicken for a full minute. Funniest damn thing I had seen in quite awhile. My mom and I fell down laughing and my dad started really getting into his role. Towards the end, my mom ran to get her camera, but she was too late–the minute ended before she was ready to shoot. So fortunately the world doesn't have to deal with photo documentation of this sordid (love that word) event. But he handled himself well, though I do believe he threw some food at her that night. Just can't remember for sure.

Then there was the "Alligator Game", which I kinda liked. I think my mom or dad invented it. We have a friend, Billy, who claims he invented it, so there is some disagreement. We only played it on weekend days when it was raining and there was nothing much to do. The concept of the game was that the whole house was infested with big alligators and they would eat you if you stepped on the floor, because that's where they lived. But if you walked on pillows, you could get to important places like the bathroom and the kitchen for food. The pillows were like islands safe from the alligators. The safest place to be was your bed. Pretty simple rules. I think the purpose of the game was that my mom and dad could spend the whole day and night in bed. These are some seriously lazy people. I got my choice of beds–theirs or mine, unless their door was locked for a bit–never quite got that part of it. Anyway, we had tons of throw pillows, seat cushions, and couch cushions, and since it was a small apartment, it was pretty easy to make little pillow trails from our bedrooms to the bathroom and kitchen. And that's the whole game. You just spend the whole day in bed watching TV or napping or eating in bed or reading or just nothing at all. I ran all over the pillows the whole day, screaming if my foot hit the floor that the alligators bit me, which made them both laugh. So, I did that a lot. We had breakfast, lunch and dinner in bed, drank in bed, watched TV, had a pizza delivered in bed (well, we did have a pillow trail to the front door) and everything. It sounds sorta stupid doesn't it? But it was actually a lot of fun and I don't even know why. We didn't play it a lot, but when we did, I had a great time. I tried to get them to play it at my school, but no one understood a goddam word I was saying except that I was fixated on alligators. Their loss. Good game. Wish we still played it.

We had lots of parties and dinners with friends at our house, along with all the houseguests who were always around, because my mom liked to cook. And so did my dad. She did mostly Cuban. He was mostly Italian and barbecue. They weren't fancy–just a ton of food put out in pots and bowls and everyone got their own food. Lots of beer and wine, too. Most of the time the other people brought their own food to share as well. Patty and Dana were always invited because they were good friends, but even more so because Patty made, in my dad's words, "The best damn sausage roll ever created." When we moved to Philly later on, they ended up being our neighbors for a couple of years right down the block from us. Talk about a coincidence. For me, it was just great to hang out with so many people. I think that's why I am such a people guy. I just love hanging out with folks, eating, drinking, lots of music and games and just talking. Some were fellow 'residents' at the hospital who worked with my dad and their wives or girlfriends, and lots of others were from my mom's school. Now these two groups of people were quite different looking and at first, they didn't mix much at the bigger gatherings like on Thanksgiving. My mom always did a big Thanksgiving for anyone who didn't have family around, which was almost all our friends and us, too. And she would make my dad and a couple of his friends deliver food for the residents who had to work in the hospital that day, which he moaned about. But he did as he was told. Anyway, at these bigger parties, the art people were pretty freaky, and some had orange or purple or pink hair, and funky clothes, and acted pretty wild. One of my favorite naked models at the school would come on roller skates and kept them on the whole time! Sadly, she was always wearing clothes, but she still looked pretty hot. But you know what? After a little time (and my mom and dad say a lot of booze), everyone started to get to know each other, and eventually these became just great parties with a whole bunch of people getting to know other people who were sort of different from them. Which is not to say that my dad's friends were like what you would expect a doctor to be. They were pretty crazy, too, but in a different way. I could tell you lots of stories about hanging out with all of them in cafes, bars, restaurants, movies, comedy clubs, parks, picnics, whatever. But then it really wouldn't be my autobiography so much, so we are not going there in detail.

But I will briefly point out that one of our friends, Vince, met his future wife, Corito, at one of our parties. See, my dad had a college friend, Big Jim, who was now living in SF and studying to be a pediatrician, and he asked if he could bring a friend, but it wasn't his girlfriend, simply a friend from the hospital. That turned out to be Corito. Well, it must have been love at first sight (I know about that stuff and it happens to me on a daily basis), because they became a couple really fast and then got married and had kids and the whole thing. We still keep in a little contact with them to this day. I bring them up for the specific reason that my dad and his friends used to play basketball on a playground on Sunday mornings a lot. And sometimes my mom and I would go watch. Not that any of them were particularly talented or even good. No dunks, lots of fouls (this guy Kerlan was noted for his ability to break people's bones and collapse lungs, due to his awkwardness), and generally unimpressive play compared to what I am used to watching in college and pro ball. But they had fun and I liked watching. Now one day, Corito came and she wasn't there to watch. She came to play! And this was before lots of women were playing basketball like they do now and man, I like women's college basketball a lot. Anyway, after a few games, turned out that my dad ended up playing against Corito and they were guarding each other. Let me just say publicly, that Corito took him to the cleaners. Shut him down completely on D (not that he was even that good at open shots), and she got her fair share of points. That was the first time in my life I realized that women could be good athletes. The thought had simply never occurred to me. I just never saw it before. So remember earlier when I said women were superior to men, except for going to sports events and wrestling? Corito changed that all around, and now about the only thing in the world I prefer doing with men is going to wrestling matches, and I hardly ever do that anymore at all.

I'm bringing all this stuff up to explain how I became the social being I am. I am bizarre, in that I never hung out with handicappers or even kids in general. Not my parent's fault. They tried to be 'good' parents and set up play dates, even before there was such a word. Kids from school, after school programs, rec center, you name it. They'd come to my house, I'd go to theirs. But when we got together, all I wanted to do was hang out with adults. I just left them to hang out with the closest adult. There was nothing my parents could do about it either. I liked all those boys and girls a lot when I was with them in school and programs and I had lots of friends, but somehow, in my mind, I always thought I was an adult. So if you gave me a choice of playing games with kids or going bowling with my parents and their friends, I would always want to go with them. Oh, I had babysitters and got left out a fair amount when I was younger, and they were cool cause they were all adults to me, but I simply never wanted to be a kid, even when I was a kid. Go figure.

I gained valuable social skills by spending most of my free time with adults–all of whom acted like children anyway. I was the unofficial bartender at all events, in charge of retrieving and opening beer bottles or getting drinks for people. I learned to open a beer bottle at about age 3.

Alright, here's one last tidbit of why I hung out with my parents and their friends all the time. My mom once threw a baby shower for someone in SF and asked my dad if it was OK, beforehand. He said fine as long as he could come, which apparently is not the way it's supposed to go. I stayed, too. It was the greatest baby shower ever given in history or so said the women before they left. And that was because my dad put a whole bunch of vodka in the punch and added something that hid the taste of it. Oh, they knew it had alcohol, they just didn't know how much. So we ended up with 30 stumbling drunk women at our house at 5 in the afternoon with a pile of baby gifts sprawled all over the living room in disarray, which my father regretted because he was made responsible for getting them all home safely. He had to call people for help, I believe. He says he would have gone to jail and been sued if he did that today. But even I got to participate and used some of my best comedy material. Like my fart line. You wanna get a laugh real quick? Just yell out at 30 drunk women, "OK, who farted?", and they will be howling with laughter. Perhaps not if they weren't drunk, but I could feel the room. My best friend, Matt, says I am a comedic genius, but I'll tell you about him later in the Philly section of the book. I sometimes use that line on crowded elevators, and goddam it, it works every time. People start to giggle and eventually break out in full laughter. At least they do in NYC and Philly. There aren't that many elevators in SF and Tucson. Anyway, I had some of that punch as well, and it was pretty tasty until I fell asleep in a corner and couldn't finish the party out. Now even I know you are not supposed to do that. But it really was the best baby shower I ever went to, and I've been to quite a few.

Chapter 8
Kicking the nun, throwing my clothes away, and getting my banana

I briefly mentioned in the beginning of this book that sometimes I did bad, but not real bad. This behavior started in SF, because that was when I became old enough to be bad. My dad says I wasn't bad at all, I was mischievous, but what the hell does that mean? So he gave me some examples and I got it right away.

Example. My mom and I were in this toy store in the Marina and I was naturally drawn to all the balls, because I simply love playing with balls. I was standing there, minding my own business, just bouncing a nice red rubber ball on the floor (about the size of a soccer ball) while my mom was looking for some gift for someone's kid. Nothing for me, mind you, but I was OK with that. Then this nun came up to me out of nowhere and grabbed the ball from me. That's right, a nun, and as you well know I had lots of nun friends in my time. Out of nowhere, she started yelling at me saying I shouldn't be touching and playing with the toys and balls, that they didn't belong to me. I mean, this nun was a fucking whack job. I had never,

ever seen a nun behave so poorly. I immediately snapped into my fight-to-get-your-ball-back mode as I told you previously, but she was too tall to punch in the mouth, too big to push over, and she had all that nun clothing on that made punching her in the stomach impossible. So I did the only think I could think of and that was to kick her in the shin and grab my ball back. Fortunately, I was wearing my really slick red cowboy boots with the pointy toes that I had just gotten for my birthday, and I hit her shin perfectly. She howled and I ran off to find my mom– I'm no fool–that nun meant trouble. So this nun found us pretty quick and started yelling at my mom that I kicked her. Here's my mom's version of the brief discussion:

Nun: "Young lady, your son just kicked me in the leg. He is a very poorly behaved child and needs to be disciplined."

Mom (who had no idea what happened): "Umm......... why did he do that?"

Nun: "I believe he didn't like it when I took away the ball he was playing with. It is not his ball, it is the store's ball, and he should know you can't just play with toys you don't own when you go into a toy story. He was making it dirty from bouncing it and could have broken something."

Mom: "So you are saying he was bouncing a ball in a store that sells balls? Trying it out?"

Nun: "Yes. But he obviously isn't buying it himself. He should be in the presence of a parent if he wants to try things out."

Mom: "Do you work here?"

Nun: "Obviously not and don't get smart with me young lady. What are you going to do about your son's behavior?"

Mom: "Well, if you took his ball away from him and he kicked you in the shin, I would say his behavior was perfectly normal and appropriate. Because you are out of your fucking mind." (My mother cusses really well–real good timing).

Nun: "Well, I never! I'm going to the manager to tell him about this."

And off she went, which was a complete waste of her time, since we were good friends with the manager of that store. I guess he calmed her down, since she left pretty quickly. When we were leaving, he asked, "What was that whole thing with the nun? She seemed nuts."

And my mom simply said, "Exactly."

Now I'm not going to bullshit you. Sometimes I was more than mischievous. Sometimes I really pissed my parents off, but always with good reason and a good heart. Perhaps the most infuriating thing I did to my parents was throwing away my clothes when I was riding a school bus or the van from Challenge to Learning or the van to and from the rec center on Saturdays. That's right, when I had clothing that I didn't like, I would plead with my parents that I hated it, and they would very calmly tell me that it was nice clothing and to give it a try. So I did. But they didn't understand until years later that I didn't hate the clothing for fashion reasons. Turns out I have very sensitive skin and lots of things make me itch or irritate my skin, or just don't feel right to me. And this includes everything: shirts, pants, socks, underwear, jackets, hats, shoes, sneakers–everything. Well, they didn't think I was smart enough to determine what clothing felt good and what didn't (morons) and assumed they could figure this out for me, without my input. Even though I know for a fact that all adults have clothing they like and dislike for various reasons and quite simply, who the hell is going to wear clothing that doesn't feel good? Nobody, that's right. But me, I gotta wear whatever the hell they give me, even if it makes me uncomfortable or downright irritated.

One day I simply reached my breaking point. I was on the school bus and this sweater I was wearing was fucking killing me. I couldn't take it anymore. So it suddenly occurred to me that if I threw it out the window, it would be gone forever and they would never find it. I was hoping they wouldn't even notice. So I took off my jacket, then took the sweater off, asked one of the bigger kids to help me open the window, and then I tossed it out. All the kids were laughing and cheering because they thought I was crazy funny. Like any comedian, I respond well to a warm audience and it occurred to me I also hated the hard brown leather shoes I was wearing as well. Out they went too. Then I sat back down smiling and content. I misjudged the possibility of no one noticing, when I threw the shoes out the window, which I regret to this day. I think I could have gotten away with a lot more before they noticed, but I gave up my whole game with the shoes.

When I got off the bus, the driver immediately saw me walking in my socks about the same time my mother was at the bus door, and he said he had no idea where my shoes were, but that I had them on when I got on the bus. So they went back to look for them, but the kids ratted me out. Not because they were ratfinks, but because they thought I was cool. When we got in the house, my mom immediately asked me where my sweater was (even though she already knew) and I told her it was with my shoes. She didn't laugh. That night, we had the big family discussion on how I couldn't do that anymore, that I was being a baby and immature and that I had to act more grownup and all that sort of crap. And I again told them that the sweater itched and the shoes hurt my feet. They said they were sorry, but I had to simply tell them when I didn't like clothes and they would take care of it. What bullshitters. I began to tell them which clothes felt good and which didn't and they spent the whole time explaining to me why they actually did feel good. I mean, am I losing you here, or what? The goddam clothes don't feel good to me, but it feels good to them and so I have to wear them? Complete lack of logic and understanding. Now I was pissed.

So after their complete lack of response to my request to simply choose which clothes felt good and which didn't, I felt obligated to express my discontent. I began to discard anything that was even remotely uncomfortable. Anywhere. In the bushes at school, in the playground, walking the streets with the Challenge to Learning folks. I quickly learned that all adults are involved in a grand conspiracy to prevent kids from doing things their parents don't want them to do. Every damn piece of clothing I tossed out in the bushes or in the garbage or left in the bowling alley always turned up, right back in my locker or desk or whatever. I couldn't get rid of anything for a while. Then it dawned on me that the only thing that worked was a moving vehicle–meaning the buses and vans again. So I returned to that strategy and with the tremendous help of my friends, I started successfully losing all clothing that I disliked.

This went well for me and poorly for them for about a month. I didn't do it every day simply because I liked lots of my clothes. But I was able to lose a whole bunch of shit pretty fast. Finally, my parents gave up. We called a truce and went into my bedroom and went through every drawer and closet and I personally identified what could stay and what had to go. There was a lot of stuff there that they liked and I didn't, but they knew it was fruitless. We cleaned the place up in a day and I had everything I liked to wear in place and all the shit was given to some charity. And to this day, no one tells me what I have to wear or not wear. I don't mean to say that I get to choose all the fashions, because they aren't into WWE replica clothing, but I generally choose all my clothes, they get a veto for looks, and if they buy me stuff, like for my birthday, I try it on, give it the thumbs up or down, and that's just the way it goes. I shop a lot on Amazon and that works great, because I get to pick stuff and if it feels crappy when I get it, I can return it and my parents don't have to run around to stores. As it should be. I'm in my 40's now and who the hell wants their parents telling them what to wear every goddam day. I simply broke free at a very early age.

Well, there was another small thing that sort of pissed off my dad. That was the mandatory banana. You see, when the van came to get me on Saturday mornings to go to the rec center, I brought a little brown lunch bag with a sandwich and some snacks. Nothing special. Except I always had to have a banana in it. I don't mean I really wanted a banana in the bag. I would not get in the van unless there was a banana in my lunch bag. We usually had bananas around so it was seldom a problem. But the first time there was no banana in the house on a Saturday morning, I refused to get in the van. I said I would stay home for the day unless I had the banana. You gotta realize it's very difficult for adults to try to have a rational discussion about a topic like this with their handicapped son, especially when the driver and all the other kids want to get going. I just wouldn't get in the van. They didn't even bother to threaten to let the van leave without me, because I damn well knew they had plans for the day that didn't include me, and they desperately wanted me to go to the rec center. Not only because it was fun and good for me, but also because they were going to be partying hard all day themselves without me. So that first time, my dad ran up the block to the corner grocery store as fast as he could and bought a bunch of bananas in about 2 minutes, with a very nice yellow banana tucked into my little brown bag. I smiled and politely said thank you and was on my way.

I imagine the subject came up with them during the day, because when I got home, my dad asked me how the banana was and I said delicious. So he handed me another one and said I could have it. I looked at him askance (that means with attitude) and said no thanks, I already had one today. Then came the inquisition. They finally realized I never ate bananas at home. They did, but I didn't. They kept harping on why I didn't eat bananas at home and only at the rec center. And I told them that I just liked them at the rec center–that was where they tasted the best. Then they looked askance at me again (is that a great word or what?). Since it was hardly a big effort to have bananas around and they both liked them, the problem only came up occasionally, but when it did, my dad just hauled his ass back up to the store to get one for me before the van arrived.

This wouldn't be much of a story had my parents not personally taken me to the rec center just before we moved to Philly. The very last Saturday. They wanted to thank everyone at the center for all they had done for me and they even brought them farewell gifts. Very sweet of them. We all had some hugs and said goodbye, but as we were leaving, one of my counselors came up to my parents, and said, "By the way, I just thought of something we all wanted to ask you. What was with the banana every week?" My dad smiled and said, "Yeah, I know, he just always said he had to have his banana with lunch. Just his little idiosyncrasy." Uh-oh, I knew this was trouble, cause everyone from the center burst out laughing. The counselor replied, "Shane doesn't eat bananas. He wouldn't eat a banana if his life depended on it. Hates 'em. He always carried it around and during lunch he gave it out as a prize or gift to one of the other kids, who liked bananas. He made a lot of friends with those bananas."

And you know what? Even my parents laughed at this. They got it. Totally.

Chapter 9
Finishing last and being with celebrities

OK, it's time to wrap up the SF years with a few final recollections.

As always, my best recollections are usually about sports and hanging out with women. So back we go to the Special Olympics, since that was a general combo. Only this time, we're talking swimming and track. Now I already told you I was a good swimmer, but I never would have won a gold in SF, because there was this guy in my district who didn't look handicapped at all and he could kick everyone's butt. Clearly a ringer, but what are you gonna do? Didn't really matter because I took dead last in every swimming race and track race I was ever in. For track, it was because I am the slowest running human being on the face of the earth. Do I care? Not in the least. I think the whole running thing is ridiculous and a waste of time and effort. If there is no ball involved in a sport, I have no interest in it (except gymnastics, of course, but I have been retired from that for many years). But I didn't really have to be last all the time. The problem was the rules. It was carefully explained to us all the time that you had to stay in your lane—those were the painted lines I had never seen before in my life until the first time we had a track meet. I fixated on the lines and when the starting gun was fired, all I could ever think about was staying between the lines. I'd run 10 yards and start veering out of my lane, stop, reset myself and get another 5 or ten yards and again start to cross the lines. I just got wrapped up in the lane thing. I stopped and started about 5 or 6 times in a 50-yard dash, which meant I would reach the finish line about a minute after everyone else. People thought it was hysterical, but I was very diligent about the whole thing. My parents didn't care as long as I was having fun, and I didn't care if I was last, as long as I stayed in the lanes, which I did. So we would all have a good laugh about it, though I really didn't see any humor in it all. Swimming was even worse, since the lines were on the bottom of the pool and these ropes on the surface. It was impossible for me to stay in my lane, I was all over the pool during every race. I always got confused and caught up in the ropes and always came in last there as well, even though I was a pretty good swimmer. But again, who really cares–it's just a game to have fun and I had fun. But admittedly, I did have more fun when I won, so I am a bit of a hypocrite (father's choice of word). Cause in the softball throw, I kicked ass and never lost in SF due to my fantastic trainer, Camilo Pascual. While the lesson may be that winning is better than losing, I am not going to write that tired old cliché that playing to the best of your ability is the most important thing. The most important things are winning and always staying in your lane.

I had a few famous moments in SF, but nothing like the Perry Como commercials. I gotta couple of stories along these lines. At the rec center, we went to summer camp (La Honda) for a couple of weeks and that was the first time I ever was away from home that long, specifically away from my parents. Course, they had abandoned me for their trip around the world, but that didn't matter much to me, cause I was with my Miami family. But when I went away, they had tremendous anxiety. I had a great time and never thought about them once, except when the counselors made us call home a few times to calm them down. It was great; traditional summer camping stuff like swimming, boating, campfires, and apparently celebrities, but I didn't recognize any of them. Since my parents weren't there, I can't give you names. I bring it up because that winter, we had a winter skiing trip in Reno, and my parents would never have let me go if I hadn't done so well at the summer camp. You see, I was one year below the age cutoff for the ski trip, which was part of the Special Olympics. But all the counselors at the rec center wanted me to go and somehow it got worked out. The one hang up was that I had no clue about skiing. Never saw it or did it, but no one seemed to care so neither did I. So the first day we're there, they put me in some skis with a person on each side of me holding my hands and we started off. I looked down the mountain and nearly shit myself. No way I was going down that thing. I went limp, completely. This would have been a cute anonymous story had there not been a camera crew from a local SF news station there everyday. So every goddam day they would shoot footage of me on my skis, holding hands with counselors, traveling about 3 feet before plopping down in the snow, shaking my head no, and refusing to stand up. This was broadcast as a human interest story on the local news in SF every night that week, with those asshole newscasters laughing at me and the whole scene. All my fucking friends, my parents' friends, and all the neighbors saw it. They thought it was really funny, but I didn't think it was funny at all when I found out about it later. On the last day, the counselors gave up and pulled me down the hill on a sled with me happily waving, which was also filmed and put on the TV, with everyone saying I had finally found my winter sport. The newscasters all had a great chuckle. Fuck them.

I did get some publicity during my time in SF, though. I got on NBC SportsWorld, some show I never watched, which was hosted that day by Sally Struthers, the woman from the All in the Family TV show, which is one of my favorite TV shows of all time. I have all the episodes on DVD. As usual, my parents didn't even know I was on it since I never told them, and again they signed some release papers they didn't read. But I think it was Vince who called them and said I was on TV, and then we all ran and gathered around to watch me sit quietly in a group of handicappers around Sally while she talked some stuff I haven't a clue about. But it was pretty funny because the whole time they were shooting, the camera guys were trying to tell me to look at something behind me and I would turn around and look back, then look at them and shrug my shoulders. Then they would keep pointing behind me and I'd look back again and put my arms up and push people aside to see what they were pointing to, but I didn't see anything. I did this about 10 times while she was talking, while everyone else was watching her without moving an inch. And of course, they filmed every moment of my confusion and plopped it right on the TV show for everyone to see. I never really got it, until my parents started laughing and asked me why I kept turning around and motioning to people and wouldn't look at Sally. That's when it clicked that they were trying to make me look at her when she was talking. Instead, I looked like a nut who was lost on the set. I was squirming and looking everywhere except where I was supposed to be looking. I guess I wasn't cut out for an acting career. Anyway, I got on TV again. And I made people laugh.

I tell you what was cool though. They had a Special Olympics Day at Candlestick Park (that's where the Giants used to play in my old days) on July 31, 1983. And they made a special poster for that day that was in the windows of thousands of storefronts throughout the Bay Area the whole month of July. And on that poster they announced that it was a Giants game, that it was Special Olympics Day, and they put the pictures of 4 people on that poster. Two of the guys were head honchos in the Special Olympics who I never met. But then there was a picture of Jack Clark, one of the great players for the Giants in those days. And guess who the fourth guy was. Yup, a picture of me with my arms raised, wearing my medals after the California Special Olympics. With my name right below the picture. I think they screwed it up a little because my picture was smaller than the others, but these things happen. Anyway, it's sort of funny that we moved from SF on June 30th, so we never actually got to see the poster there. Then a friend called and told my parents about it, and said it sure looked like me on the poster. My dad had the nerve to say, "I doubt it, the kids sort of all look alike." What a racist he can be. But then the friend, I think it was Bruce, said, "Well, it's got his name on it too." And then he mailed one to us and sure enough, me and Jack Clark represented the Special Olympics that fine day. I bet if I had still lived there, I coulda gone to the game and maybe gotten on the field with him. But I had bigger moments with sports fame later on in Philly, so it turned out just fine. And that poster is still hanging in a frame on my bedroom wall to this day.

And yes, I did meet some celebrities in SF, mostly ones who lived in our neighborhood. I could drop names that my parents knew, but I didn't recognize many of them. They were all nice to me, though. But the one guy I bumped into a bunch of times was MORK. His name was Robin Williams, and he was the nicest and funniest guy in the world. I don't think he knew my name or even recognized me each time we met (well maybe he did at the fish store, cause we seemed to bump into him there a lot), but he would always go out of his way to be funny and make me laugh and do

Mork stuff and everything. I was really sad to hear he died recently. He was a really good guy to me and I liked a lot of his movies, especially "Jack", which is about a boy who looks like a man. Sort of like me.

The Philly Years

Chapter 1
Some schools suck

So end of June, my parents flew me to Miami to hang out with Hector and Elena for a couple of weeks, because they were driving all our stuff in a rental truck across the entire United States of America, towing this crappy car that replaced our beloved VW van, and they knew it would be a long haul and wanted to spare me the effort. Solid folks, my parents. I can think of nothing good to be said about that sort of trip. We were moving to Philly because my dad finally became a real doctor and was going to finally get a real job. I have no idea why he picked Philly, but boy, am I glad he did. Philly is where I really became who I am today. It's my hometown forever, just like my dad says he is a New Yorker forever, even though he hasn't lived there for almost 40 years. Some things just get into your brain and they never leave, I guess.

Apparently, their trip out to Philly was a disaster and it took them way longer than expected and there are lots of great stories they tell people about that trip. And everyone laughs their asses off. But I wasn't there, so they can save it for their own book.

When we finally reunited in Philly (my mom flew down to Miami and got me), I remember the shock at seeing our new house. It was a big, old beautiful house in a town on something called the Main Line (no clue what that means, but it's just outside Philly), made of thick stone (granite, I'm told), a stone roof (called slate), a big front and back yard, and huge trees. It was like out of a movie. I was very impressed. Then I went inside and it was a complete dump. Peeling wallpaper, a kitchen that looked like it had been in a fire, dirt everywhere–you get the picture. And get this, there had been a murder in that house a few years back–now that was very cool. See, though my dad was a doctor, he was still a poor doctor, and my mom was still a student, getting ready to get something called an MFA at the University of Pennsylvania. That's sort of like the graduation certificate I got after elementary school I think.

But that first summer was great. My dad had to start working right away at a hospital, but then all sorts of people came to the house and started to fix it up. I mean really fix it up. Big machines to sand and repair these great wood floors, whole new kitchen and baths, and later on, at night and on weekends, even my mom and dad worked on it, with a little help from me. We painted that whole house by the end of the first year, my dad built new big garage doors, and we worked on the yard. We were real homeowners. I never thought my parents had it in them and it turns out that was the first real house that my dad and I had ever lived in.

There's lots more I could tell you about fixing up a house, but frankly, who gives a shit except the people who live in the house. Other than the fact I had a huge bedroom and a TV/playroom room for myself. And I got to ride my Big Wheel all over the house like a madman, just like the kid in the movie, "The Shining", which is one of my favorite movies of all time, because I think it's a funny comedy and my parents think it is a scary movie. I just don't get it–seems really hysterical to me. My parents got lots of space, too–they got their darkroom as usual and my mom got studio space to paint in. It all seemed pretty good to us.

And right down the street was the elementary school I was going to go to. It had a great playground, lots of grass, and my parents and I went there a lot that first summer to play Frisbee, shoot hoops, kick a soccer ball around, and just have fun. Didn't seem like the friendliest sort of place–some other kids there did the usual staring shit and a couple of them called me 'retard', but I figured I would charm them all once school started, and couldn't have cared less.

Until I went to start school. My parents and I went in there at the end of the summer and then they sent us to some office building a few miles away to get me situated properly. That turned out to mean that I wasn't going to the nice little school across the street, I was going to be sent to a different school. They said there weren't enough handicappers for them to have 'special' classes in the school across the street and that I would get a bus to another school which I would really like. Seemed OK to me, but my mom and dad didn't look so happy. I'll shorten this up a bit because I don't know the details well and my dad can help me fill you in. So I end up on a fucking bus for 1 hour and 15 minutes each way to go to a far away school in a completely different school district. Had to get up at insane early morning hours and was usually asleep on the bus by the time I got there. Same thing coming home–was usually passed out asleep by the time I got home and was tuckered out. My mom and dad met with my teacher there. She seemed OK to me (I give everyone the benefit of the doubt when I first meet them), but my mom and dad said she was an idiot. Which did, in fact turn out to be true. Because after about a month of me coming home in a generally foul mood due to the long rides and general lack of fun at school, a day finally came when I got home crying. My mom and dad worked hard to figure out what had happened, but I had a hard time explaining it to them except that I got in trouble with that teacher for dancing in class. They looked at each other in astonishment–that's a word I don't know, but I know the look.

That night, my dad called his partners from the hospital and said he had an emergency and that he wouldn't be able to come to work until the afternoon. He really liked those guys (Joe and Norm) and they were real nice about letting him skip work to help me out. I liked those guys, too–solid citizens for a whole bunch of reasons that can go in my dad's autobiography, but I wanted the fact that they were great guys put in my book as well.

So the next morning, we all went to my school an hour away, although it took us about an hour and a half, which seemed the same as my bus ride. I watched my dad carefully and he was doing this thing he does that's called 'seething'–it's when you are really pissed off, but you don't start yelling. You just sit there and look really pissed off. Seems a waste of time to me.

When we get to the school, we headed directly to my class and teacher–I honestly can't remember the name of the teacher or school–none of us can. And my mom and dad weren't very friendly to that teacher, who at first said we needed to make an appointment to see her. My dad said something nasty to her and suddenly she said it was fine to come in and talk to her, and we all went to some little room somewhere. My parents asked her why I came home crying at all and specifically, what was the whole thing about me crying about dancing in class. And this teacher showed my mom and dad the two characteristics that they consider the deadliest combination of traits that any human can have at the same time. They are called 'arrogance' and 'ignorance'. I obviously did not have real input into this analysis, but I gotta think whatever they thought about this teacher was right on, cause I thought she was a moron as well. And to demonstrate her arrogance and ignorance, she was so stupid that she actually told my parents exactly what happened, thinking she was capable of rational thought and that she was acting as a normal thinking teacher. Which, according to my parents and later, real lawyers, was in fact, grossly illegal.

So after the question got posed, this idiot teacher actually said the following, smiling and chuckling the whole time:

"Oh my gosh! Is that what this is about?" And she smiled some more. "Oh that was just a minor incident, I'd already forgotten about it. It really wasn't a big deal at all. I am not mad at Shane at all. He just had a minor discipline for misbehavior."

And my dad, who was now more than seething, "What misbehavior?"

"Well, I put some music on the record player for the class and Shane got up next to his desk and did a little dance to the music which made all the other children laugh. It was very disruptive."

"He got up and danced? This is a problem?" said my mom.

"Well, he actually did it two times, the second time after I had already told him to stop. So I had to give him a time out."

My dad didn't really relax, but seemed to ease up a bit. "So this is about getting up for a bit and dancing to music? Well, you have to understand, he has been in schools and programs his entire short life where they ENCOURAGED dancing to music and having fun. Perhaps we can work out an understanding with him on this, but exactly how long was he 'disruptive'?"

"Oh, only about 10 or 15 seconds both times. He sat down right away when I yelled at him both times. And then he got a timeout and that was it. Not really a big deal. I'm surprised he was so upset."

I looked at my parents and could tell they were not happy and my dad was getting that really strange look he sometimes gets, when you really don't want to hang out with him.

"So what exactly was the time out thing?"

And she cheerily replied, "Well, he had to eat his lunch for an hour by himself. But he was safely locked in a room in the basement."

Suddenly, my dad stood up from his chair, which he knocked over. This really startled that lady.

"You fucking locked him up in a basement room by himself for an hour? With no fucking way out and no supervision? Are you fucking insane?"

Now the teacher seemed a little nervous, mostly because I think she knew that there was a significant chance my dad was going to punch her lights out. He can have a temper. But he is a real sexist and won't hit women, not that he gets in fights a lot. I personally would have no problem hitting a girl, say, if she took my ball on the playground. Moot point.

And she said, "He was completely safe in that locked room—no one could bother him and I looked in the window to check on him several times. He was fine. I can show you the room, it's very nice."

So this moron took us to the basement and showed us the very room she locked me in which had a table and a few chairs and nothing else.

"See. It is heated and perfectly comfortable."

"Was he crying?"

"Well, of course he was crying. That's the whole point of the punishment. To make him think about it and improve his behavior."

My parents clearly didn't know what to do, at this point. Oh, they knew exactly what they were going to do in the big picture (as I learned later), but I could see the wheels turning in their minds and they were trying to figure out what to do with this woman in this moment. I realized quickly that no one was going to get hit, but I figured there would be a lot of screaming, but then it stopped with only one final statement from my dad to that teacher, which I can't write as he said it, and I don't think he can even remember exactly what he said, but I know the words "fucking moron", "incompetent asshole", and "fucking bitch" were definitely used.

And we left that school that very moment and I never had to go back there again my whole life.

Chapter 2
When giving up is the best idea

My dad didn't go to work for two days and my mom skipped her school as well, but he was in and out of the house a whole bunch of times. And on the phone a lot, calling a lot of people. Which was sort of strange, cause we didn't really have a lot of friends to call at that time. We had only been living there for like 3 months. Turns out, he was spending all his time trying to find a school for me. And I guess, he struck out on that, because I never tried out any other public schools. For a brief moment, it appeared I might become Catholic again, because there was one of those schools pretty close to our house and we ran over the second afternoon to look at it and it was OK, but nothing special. Then the nun we met (who was pretty nice, actually), said something that made my dad's head snap back–I really saw his head snap. Never saw that move before. I copied it for a while–it was a great move to give when you are surprised. She said they were filled up and had something called a 'waiting list'. That means there was no spot for me now and that I had to get at the end of the line for kids who also wanted to go to that school. And she said it likely wouldn't happen at least until next year.

I found out later that my dad spent two hours on the phone that very night with a lawyer from Washington, DC at his home there. My dad says he was a really smart and good guy. Not just cause he knew everything about the law and special education, but cause he also had something called 'common sense and wisdom'. My parents say I have a lot of this, but I'm not smart enough to really comment on that.

My father told the lawyer everything that had happened. About the school across the street not having special ed because there weren't enough special kids, about the Catholic special ed school having a waiting list because there were too many special ed kids in the area without any place to go, about my 3 hours on the bus each day getting sent to some far away school, about how that teacher was an asshole and locked me in the basement. And about how the whole district blew him off no matter who he called.

And you know what that lawyer told my dad? Remember, this is early 1980's so I don't know if the rules are the same anymore–my dad says I have to add that 'qualifier'. He said my dad was absolutely right on everything. He said lots of school districts in lots of places "farmed out" special ed kids to other school districts–sounds like a baseball term to me. Then they paid those schools a certain amount of money to teach those kids special ed. Now get this–what they paid those other schools to take their special kids was a lot less than what they collected from the State of Pennsylvania to 'organize' my education. So it was a scam–even I understand that now, but I didn't know that then. They made money by shipping me out to that shithole. And the long bus ride was illegal, too. Couldn't be over 45 minutes each way. And he was sure there were more than enough special ed kids around to get a class together for my local school, but that would require something called a "class action" lawsuit that meant a lot of the other parents in our school district with handicappers would have to join my father in a big lawsuit. He said it was his experience that most parents wouldn't do that, cause they usually had other normal kids in the public schools and they didn't want to make trouble that might affect their other kids. My dad didn't believe this at first, but the lawyer simply said my father had no clue of the types of things a school district can do to your normal kids if they think a family or families are troublemakers. My parents were shocked. I was fine, because I was hanging out in the new house and there were lots of boxes being delivered for the ongoing renovations, and playing in big boxes (like refrigerator boxes) is a hell of a lot better than going to a shithole school.

Now my dad and I never proved that what the lawyer said was true in my case, but my dad says he believed it absolutely was true.

Being the hothead idiot he is, my dad immediately wanted to sue the school district–that means go to court like with Judge Judy–and try to get things fixed right and proper. That was when the lawyer was wise and showed common sense. He asked my dad, "Do you really want to spend the next 6 or 7 years of your life and spend a lot of money fighting this fight, winning it, and watch your son have a miserable school life during that whole time, and then end up getting sent to a school 45 minutes away, instead of an hour and a half. Because that's what could easily happen. And it will be hard to prove any harm regarding his being locked in the basement, despite the barbarity (cool word) of it all. I'll be happy to work with you, because people do need to fight against this, but my professional recommendation to you is to get the hell out of that place and find a better place to live for your family and specifically, your son."

My dad is seldom speechless, but he was awful quiet for a long time after that call. My mom and dad didn't go to sleep that whole night (I think), and spent the night around the kitchen table talking calmly and softly. I slept like a king, myself, but I didn't have their problems.

The next day, my parents happened to talk about things with our next door neighbor who was a very wealthy retired businessman and his wife, who had already become very friendly with us (dinners and BBQ's), and they knew a lot about the whole area and town, cause he was also involved in politics a little. And you know what he said? "You need to get the hell out of here."

Chapter 3
Danny Ainge is not an asshole

Now there is a saying that completely baffles me: Every cloud has a silver lining. Not even a clue what that means. Could be in French for all I know. But I reminded my dad about the one great memory of this time period, and he said that line. Doesn't seem to fit from my perspective, but what the hell do I know about sayings.

It started at dinner one October night, after all this school shit started. We were eating dinner and everyone was trying to keep their spirits up–I was doing my best routines–but for some reason my dad was really down.

So out of nowhere, my mom simply said, "I'm going to take Shane to see the Sixers practice."

My dad looked at her and replied, "And how are you going to do that?"

"I'll call them and ask."

"Well, good luck, but not a chance."

Now when I heard the name Sixers, I almost fell out of my chair. I had been a Philadelphia 76'ers fan since I was first able to understand basketball back in SF. Oh, we went to some Warriors games in SF and they were fun, but the

Sixers were Julius Erving (Dr. J), Moses Malone, Mo Cheeks, Andrew Toney, Bobby Jones, I mean these guys are the greatest players ever, especially Dr. J and Moses. So I looked at my parents and said, "Can we go see them?"

My dad looked at my mom, shrugged and said, "Now you've really raised his hopes." I'm telling you, the man was really down at the time.

So my mom makes some calls and gets this guy named Harvey Pollack on the phone, who was a honcho with the Sixers. And not a good guy–a GREAT guy. And she explains the situation briefly to him about me–not that I'm in a shitty school situation, but that I am a huge fan and a handicapper and want to watch the Sixers practice, and we just moved here from SF. Apparently, he simply said, "Do you want to come next week, likely Tuesday or maybe Thursday?" And that was that. Done deal.

When my dad got home that night, my mom waited until we were all eating dinner and very matter-of-factly, with a very sly grin (my dad's description) said, "Oh, by the way, Shane and I are going to watch the Sixers practice next Tuesday."

I can't give you the details of the rest of the conversation, but my dad got more excited than me, I think. He needed his spirits raised more than me, too. You gotta remember, this was the defending World Champion Sixers who had just won the whole NBA championship the season before. And my mom added, "And I told them there would be three of us. He is a very, very nice man." So my dad spoke with his good guy partners at the hospital, got the day off, and that next Tuesday, we were off.

I don't know how it works today, but in those days, the Sixers practiced at the St. Joseph's University Fieldhouse, not at the Spectrum, where they played games. I knew about the Spectrum then, cause we were getting some 'limited' season tickets to see about a dozen Sixers games that year–

we didn't have the time to go to every game, but I would have. I hadn't heard about Saint Joe's before because I wasn't from Philly, but nowadays I know alot about them because they play basketball against my favorite team of all time, every year, the Temple Owls. I'll be talking a lot about them later. Temple, that is.

Anyway, we drove right up close, parked, and walked in the door and told the security guy that we were invited to watch practice and gave him Harvey Pollack's name. He must have been pretty important, because the guy immediately looked at his papers, saw our names and brought us directly onto the court to the sideline, where we met Harvey. I know he wouldn't ever remember me, but I remember him. What a great guy and so friendly. He said we could have any seat in the whole fieldhouse, and it turned out, we were the only guests in the entire place. So we sat front row right at midcourt. In fact, the only other people there besides Sixers' people were a few sportswriters, or so my dad said.

The first thing I noticed that I had never really known was how big these guys are. I mean when you watch them on TV or even at a game, unless you are standing on the floor with them, they all look the same size, and I had never stood on the floor with them before. They were giants.

Watching the practice was great and some of the players even waved or winked and said hello to me, right during practice. But when practice was over, Harvey brought us down on the court to meet the players!! I'm talking all the players!!! And Dr. J cracked up when I looked all the way up at his face, which was a very long way from my face, and said, "You are really fucking tall." Dr. J passed me the ball a couple of times at the basket and let me dribble around him and even between his legs and said I was a cute guy. He cracked up when I got around him and standing in front of me was Moses Malone, who promptly picked me up over his head and I slam dunked it. That's right, I slam dunked it after driving by Dr. J. With Moses Malone holding me up. There are not many people who can say that. Everyone was so nice. Harvey asked me if I wanted a basketball signed by all the players and I thought my dad was going to pass out when I said nah, I just wanted to play ball with them. And to this day, he berates me (that means he's still pissed off) for not getting that signed basketball. So we played around for another 5 minutes or so and then they all headed to the showers and waved goodbye and I was in heaven. Suddenly this really nice player came up to me and said to wait a few minutes, he wanted to walk me to the car. Well, I didn't know who he was, I didn't know his number or his face and that was because he was a rookie named Sedale Threatt. Who went on to have a really nice, long career in the NBA–I never forgot that day and followed him on TV for many years, even when he was a star for the LA Lakers who I was taught to hate by my father, along with the Boston Celtics. Father-son thing I guess. So we waited around, thanked Harvey about 100 times, my dad got to talk for a minute or two with Coach Billy Cunningham who was very nice as well, and when Sedale came out he gave me a headband and wristbands and some other cool stuff. And then he walked us to our car and high fived me and said I was going to grow up and be a basketball star. Well, I must admit I knew he was bullshitting me on being an NBA star, but I thought I might have a shot at the Special Olympics. Never happened.

Oh yeah, one more bball story since I'm on the Sixers, and probably won't get back to them again in this book, since there is too much other stuff to cover. We went to lots of Sixers games over the years, but there was one game that changed my dad's life forever. It was a couple of years later and a big game: Sixers against their mortal enemy, the Boston Celtics. Now, when you have a team that you love (Sixers), you have to hate the team that is their archrival–that means the team that they most want to beat whenever they play them. In those days, that meant the Celtics. And on each team, the fans have to pick one particular player to hate more than any other. You don't really hate the other team or any player personally. You just have to root real hard that they get their asses kicked and they are humiliated. Then they can go home and have a nice dinner. These are simply the rules of being a fan, as explained by my dad.

For Boston fans, my dad explained that Andrew Toney was the most hated and he got the nickname, "The Boston Strangler", for almost always scoring a ton of points and almost personally kicking their asses. For Sixers fans, Danny Ainge was the same–he always played big and everyone hated him for a bunch of reasons I really didn't understand, but I didn't care much about that stuff–I was just thrilled to go to all the games.

So we're at this game, but not sitting in our usual seats, which were OK, but these seats were 3rd row directly behind the Celtics bench–some friend gave my dad the seats. We could hear every word they said; it was so cool. We got there real early to watch warm-ups because we knew the seats were so close and this was a rare chance. Anyway, all the Celtic guys were shooting and stretching and the usual stuff and even though we had all agreed to hate the Celtics, it's pretty hard to hate and not be impressed by people like Larry Bird, Robert Parrish, and Kevin McHale. I tried to yell at Kevin McHale that I watched him in college when we lived in Minnesota, but he didn't hear me or didn't understand me and I couldn't get his attention. Unfortunately, for my dad, Danny Ainge did notice me yelling. And then he came over, smiling at me, and I gave him my biggest smile and a big thumbs up. He walked around the bench and came right up to me and my parents and said hello and then we did a high five and he said I was the cutest guy he had ever seen. I was eating a hot dog at the time with a lemonade and he said that it looked really delicious and I said it was. Then for some reason, I held it up to him and asked him if he wanted a bite. I like to share. He didn't hesitate for a second. Just said sure and get this, he took a nice bite of my hot dog, right from where I left off. He wasn't worried about the cooties or anything and didn't go to the other end of the hot dog. Then he asked if he could wash it down and I handed him my lemonade and he drank it straight from my straw—again no cooties worries for him. He lifted me up and tickled me for a few seconds and then said he had to go but that his first basket was going to be for me. I said thank you.

My dad says he must have assumed we were Celtics fans since we were sitting behind their bench. He came up with several other pathetic excuses, but eventually had to face the fact that Danny Ainge was a really nice guy, not an asshole. And that he could never hate him again, ever. Couldn't even root against him ever again. Sorta had to root for him a bit, though he never admitted to that. Danny Ainge was still in the sports news and on TV for many years afterwards. And whenever he came on the TV, my dad would shake his head and say, "I can't believe he is such a NICE guy. It's killing me." Still happens occasionally.

Chapter 4
Going for my Masters of Fine Arts

I had no problem with my changing schools at all. Because the very next week, I started my program for an MFA at the University of Pennsylvania, along with my mother.

Probably the second best school I ever attended. Got me a nice piece of my mom's studio to do my drawings and colorings. First thing in the morning when we arrived, we would go to this big school bus called "Le Bus" and I would get milk and a bread and butter sandwich for breakfast, and my mom would get coffee and a muffin. That bus later became a whole restaurant, but when I started going there, it was still just a bus with great food in it–and hippie people running it, which reminded me of Al's in Minneapolis (the people, not the places). There were lots of great places around there to eat, with lots of hot dog carts and other food carts as well, but hot dogs are pretty much at the top of my food list to this day. My dad says they are very good for you–very healthy. And as you know, he's a doctor and would know. And really friendly people at those carts who got to know me so well over time, that eventually I would visit them by myself (about a year later) and they would just give me whatever I asked for, and my mom would go down and pay them later. That's called trust. I forgot to mention that most of the people in the town where our house was were assholes and didn't have trust. They didn't like handicappers at all. But I will say we had great neighbors on three sides of that house. Rest of the town pretty much sucked. OK, I think I made my point.

Within a week, there was an old couch in my mom's studio for my naps, a little chair and desk for me to use, and free roaming rights in the Fine Arts building, though I wasn't allowed to go up the street to the hot dog guy to get a bite by myself until a year later, as I already mentioned. Not that I stayed in the MFA program that long. But I did stay there for about 4 or 5 months and it was great. Not as many naked women models as SF, but plenty of cool artist type people. One of the reasons I got the run of the place was that the head of the whole place immediately took a shine to me and me to him. His name was Neil Welliver and he was a famous painter. After a short time, we became really good friends and I would sometimes walk around with him when he went to each of the students' studios to look at their work. Most of the time when we walked in, he would turn to me and say, "Shano, what do you think of this work?" I got to give it a thumbs up or down. And I swear to you, whatever gesture I gave, Neil would follow it to the letter and either trash the work or praise it, according to my judgment—he was a real character. It became so well known, that soon, people were bribing me with food and little things to come into their studios and get me to give them a thumbs up. Which I often did, cause I believe in bribes. But sometimes, they just sucked and I had to give them the thumbs down and they wouldn't be too happy. But everyone there treated me on the up and up, and I felt like I was in the right school for that time.

Now Neil and his wife, Shelia, soon became friends of

all of us and we sometimes went out to dinner with them. Later we went to their home in Maine to hang out with them and my parents even went to their cabin way up on the Canadian border for fishing and stuff. They knew lots of famous people that I never heard of and gave great dinner parties and such. Neil and my dad and a really cool dude named Frank, generally got drunk, trying to show who was the better drinker, but it turned out that Frank's wife, Yasio (they were from Japan) could hold her booze better than any of them. She never got so drunk as to act like an idiot, which I cannot say about the other three. My mom hardly drunk at all back then. But I digress yet again. They were really good people and helped me out a lot. On my 18th birthday, my mom happened to have an art show at the Blue Mountain Gallery in NYC and sure enough, Neil and Shelia came down to celebrate my birthday with me and gave me a big birthday dinner party at a really fancy NYC restaurant. There were famous people there too, but none of them played any pro or college sports, so I didn't know who the hell they were. But they were all really nice to me, which goes to show that famous people are not all assholes as some people say (just like Danny Ainge)–most of the famous people I've met have been really nice to me, even though I don't even know why they are famous or even remember their names. Neil is dead now, but we still keep in touch with Shelia, who is one of the sweetest people in the world. I really miss her but she lives far away in several places around the world like Ireland (where my good friend Patrick is from), Maine, and I think even somewhere in South America, though I am not sure. And they had really nice kids to hang with (especially John, who played with me up in Maine), but I haven't seen them in a long time since we moved to Tucson when I was around 22.

Anyway, my months at Penn were great, and I ended up hanging out there a lot over the next 3 years, even after my parents found me a real school that had special ed, and that they thought was good for me. That might sound simple enough, but it wasn't. Remember, we were fixing up that great house, but now we were getting it ready to sell, because we all hated where that house was placed. Too bad the town sucked; it was a great house. It irritated my parents so much to live there and was such a pain in the ass driving back and forth between the city of Philly and the Main Line, that we ended up renting an apartment for a year in the Old City section of Philadelphia, while looking for a new house in the center of Philadelphia, which we all realized very quickly was actually where we should have moved in the first place. None of us were cut out to be suburbanites. Just the way it is. So much for parental judgment and decision-making.

Chapter 5
Finally, a great school

Our new apartment in Old City was called a loft. Big room, high ceilings, small kitchen and a bathroom. Funky but not like the house we were trying to unload. But I thought it was great. It was big enough to have a baseball catch inside or throw the football around, which generally annoyed my mom, especially when we broke stuff, but all in all, I liked that place. I am easy to please, either because I like every place or because my parents pick good places. Take your pick. I really don't know.

But it was time to start the search for a new school for me, this time in the City of Philadelphia. And my parents did their studying and research and came to a rather bizarre conclusion after visiting a bunch of people and schools. The best school for me was the George Washington Elementary School in South Philly. I'm not talking the name of the school cause I know a little about George Washington, the cherry tree, and the dollar bill. I'm talking about a bunch of other things that made them a bit nervous with their own decision. Washington Elementary School was in what was called a dangerous part of town, across the street from two very tall buildings called housing projects (Southwark Towers, for those from Philly), though those towers were torn down awhile back. According to my sources, there was lots of crime in the area, lots of drugs, gangs, drive-by shootings, and it was a mostly black area. This last aspect was not really a concern for my parents. But for me, that was a hugely positive factor, since I am a racist and prefer black people to others and consider myself black to this day. I am repeating myself, I know. For emphasis. So for me, I was returning to my brothers.

How bad was that neighborhood? Well, here's a quick story that took place about 10 years later, after I wasn't even in that school anymore. My mom and I were going to the 9th Street Italian Market which was not that far from there, but we had to park very far away, because we couldn't find a parking space anywhere. So after we finished at the Market and were heading back to our truck, we were walking down a side street and my mom looks ahead and sees a gang of guys on the next street corner. And they were selling drugs to people in cars who were pulling up. These were a few of the more important things I learned from my school days, cause some of the older kids in my school were selling drugs even when I was in school. It was a K–8 school, and some of the older kids looked like full-grown men to me at the time. Anyway, we crossed the street cause my mom felt it was 'safer', but I didn't feel scared at all. Then all of a sudden, a couple of the gang guys yelled out, "Shano, my man!!!" My mom got this strange look on her face and suddenly all the guys ran across the street to see us. It was some of my old friends from Washington Elementary School! We all gave the brother handshake (I am not allowed to tell, it's a secret I think), and everyone was so happy to see each other that we were laughing and even telling a few stories to my mom, who had no clue what was going on. Then one of the guys said, "You know, this isn't a good place for you guys to be walking around. We'll walk you to your car, cause there are some problems we're having with this other gang right now."

And my mom said, smiling and only a little bit more relaxed said, "That's very nice of you guys, but I really don't want to be involved in a drive-by shooting in a gang war. Maybe we should walk by ourselves."

But they wouldn't hear of it. "No way that's going to happen, ma'am. Just walk in the middle of us. Any of us would take a bullet for Shano. He is the man."

So they surrounded us and walked us a couple more blocks to our truck. They told my mom some stories about us in school and I was so happy to see some of them. Others I just didn't know. But they were great guys and when we got to the truck, we did our special handshakes and even some hugs and they all told me to take care. And my mom thanked them.

True story, I swear. Ask my mom. Still scares the crap out of her.

According to my parents, they liked the school because they had lots of special ed classes in the school, which meant that all the 'normal' kids and regular teachers were comfortable seeing handicappers around all the time. My dad says it was about 10% special ed–that means 1 out of every 10 kids were special ed. So people generally did less of the staring thing and were sort of comfortable with us. Not completely, but I'll get to that later. My parents really liked that and so did I. They thought the principal (her name was Judy) was 'with the program' and something called 'progressive', and when they met my potential first teacher, Ms. Nancy Lovitch, they liked her as well. Plus, the school was just introducing computers into special ed, which they really liked, because they said that was the future. And they were right. And just as an aside, I became a computer wiz (well, at least for a handicapper) and learned to use computers at that school beginning with an Apple II, and quickly moving on to a Mac. We're writing this book on MY Chromebook. I became good at video games, too. Almost every system. It changed my life forever. It was the best school I ever went to.

It was also the craziest school I ever went to, and I have a bunch of stories to tell you. You won't believe some of them, but I'm telling you it's all true. You simply have to believe me.

My first day at school is a good example. My mom and I got there late around 10 am, because the principal told us to come at that time, so she could do some paperwork stuff and show me around and talk to my mom about the whole set-up. So all the classes had started and when we got to the school, the street in front was deserted. Except for a gang of about 6 black guys in their 20's standing right in front of the school. The front of the school was a loading zone, but that was cool for us because my mom drove a little red Mazda pickup truck and it had special license plates that let us park in loading zones, which was very convenient when you went to the movies or just about anywhere in Philly. My dad showed me the plates and the signs and explained the whole thing to me. Sweet.

So I looked at my mom and she looked nervous. Downright scared might be a better word. As she started to pull up to the front of the school, I started to wave hello to the guys and she abruptly yelled at me to keep quiet and not move. It was one of those moments where I knew to shut up. She very slowly tried to pull up to the very front door of the school, so we could get in quickly. But the guys hanging out on the sidewalk turned and started to watch her pull up. Suddenly, one guy, a real big dude, stepped off the curb and walked right in front of the truck, and put his hand out to make my mom stop. My mom stopped the truck instantly and I could see she didn't know what to do and now she really was scared. The big dude slowly walked from the front of the truck to my mom's window (which was closed–it was cold, man), rapped on the window and motioned to her to roll the window down. He wasn't smiling and neither was my mom. But she slowly rolled down the window about one inch without saying a word. And the big dude very calmly said, "Don't pull in any further, there's a broken bottle in the gutter here and you'll cut your tires."

My mom gave him a pathetic smile and thanked him and turned off the truck where it was. The dude returned to the group standing right next to the truck, pretty much uninterested in us anymore. Once I saw my mom smile and thank him, I knew the coast was clear, and when we got out, much to my mom's dismay (great word), I ran over to them and said hi and put out my hand to give him five. They all laughed and they all high fived me and said, "how you doin', little man". And then they went back to their talking and we went inside. My mom was paler than Casper the ghost. And that's how I arrived at school the first day.

So we got the tour and all, and I met my new teacher, Ms. Lovitch, and the teacher's aide, Sarah. I liked them both, but Sarah became my best buddy in that class. She made me laugh and I made her laugh. I was only in that class for the rest of the year before I moved up the following year, but Sarah and I were friends for the whole time I was there, probably around 7 or 8 years. Which is longer than I should have been there, but I'll explain that later in detail–it's a great story. We always said hello and hung out in the halls together whenever we bumped into each other during those later years. Great lady–the coolest. The kids in my class were all pretty cool too–a few were more handicapped than others, but there were plenty of kids to hang with, play games, and the class was actually fun. Now when they played music, they WANTED you to get up and dance. They wanted you to sing in music class as loud as you could. They wanted you to blow your flutophone to your heart's content. And play as hard as you could on the playground and in gym class. Get this: They wanted you to have fun at school while you were learning. How about that as a concept. Finally, my parents did something right.

After the first week of getting to know everyone and having fun to boot, it was time for my 'psychological and intellectual testing' which was then used for my IEP (Individualized Education Plan). Obviously I had no clue what the hell they were doing, but I knew it was of some importance since my dad took off from work to attend with me and my mom. That generally indicates importance, though on several occasions he embarrassed himself and me, with his presence. Like a few years later, when the IEP was developed to have me learn to write cursive (which I sucked at and never really learned–so much for plans). When they said they thought I was ready to learn cursive writing, my dad looked puzzled and absent-mindedly said, "What exactly do you mean by cursive?" You have to realize that my dad sometimes misses the simplest things cause he is usually thinking about 4 things at the same time and can be easily confused. They all looked at him like he was crazy and one woman said, "You know, write in SCRIPT." And my dad, his face really red answered, "Oh, I knew that."

Anyway, back to the first testing day. This guy (called a psychologist) started asking me to do stuff that seemed really stupid to me. Like he had three big wood blocks: a square, a circle, and a triangle, and asked me to put them in their places in a ridiculously stupid puzzle. I mean a cockroach could do that. He wasn't very good at understanding my speech, so I think I got a big X somewhere on his sheet for that problem, even though my mom and dad and even a couple of other people in the room understood me. Just not him. So I decided to screw around and get some laughs. I put the triangle on the circle cutout, the square on the triangle, and the circle on the square. Just balanced them perfectly. He nodded and made another X on his paper and asked me to try again. Four more times. I tried to carefully avoid putting the pieces in the right place and a couple of times I accidentally put them in the correct place, but quickly removed them and made sure they were always screwed up. He made a funny face after the fifth time and wrote some more. My dad tried to interrupt and tell me to stop screwing around, but the guy told him he couldn't help me and that he had to accept my limitations. I think my dad's face was turning purple. It was really funny. Then the guy put some stuff out and said, "Shane, put the pencil in the cup, put the eraser next to the cup, and then move the cup to the other side of the table." Which was the dumbest thing I ever heard. So I just moved the cup to the side of the table where he wanted it and put the pencil and eraser both in the cup, because why would you leave the eraser out of the cup if you were putting the shit away. Made no sense to me. He made some marks on his paper, and my dad kept trying to interrupt and say I was screwing around, but no one would allow him to keep talking, so he had to keep his mouth shut, which was hysterical. This went on for like 40 minutes or so and then we left. They said we would get the full report in a few days and have another meeting. When we came back, I apparently had the IQ of the pencil, and according to their numbers I shouldn't have been able to breathe on my own, let alone communicate with any living creatures. My dad was flipping out, but my mom kept calm. When we finally finished we met alone with some other woman who I think was higher up than the guy, and she was laughing and said, "Oh don't worry about those scores. Shane is doing fine, the testing was ridiculous, and he is going to continue doing exactly all the things he is studying right now. It's just paperwork to keep everyone busy." Which made my mom smile, but my dad was annoyed and said, "Yeah, but now it's on his record as his IQ. What the hell does that mean?" And the woman replied, "Absolutely nothing because I already made out his IEP according to how he was doing in class, which is just fine. And he will get tested every year forever, so the scores will be all over the place. Though it might hurt him when he applies to college." She had a good sense of humor.

Ms. Lovitch was an excellent teacher and did a fine job working on my letters and numbers with me, and we all had fun in that class. She gets big thumbs up and I would have more to say about her, but since I was only there that year and my next teacher would change my life completely, I don't have a lot of specific memories of funny things. Funny stuff happened for sure, just can't remember it well. My apologies to all.

Beth was my speech therapist and she was really funny. My speech always goes up and down with my hearing, which sucks and always gets better and worse for some reason I don't understand. For instance, it always gets worse now in the summer in Tucson when I swim every day. Maybe it's the wax, but I'm no doctor. But I never wear hearing aids cause they screech all the time and if you've ever had that happen to you, you would understand the logic of my decision. I hear well enough to get by just fine, though I think my TV volume sometimes drives my parents crazy. I just shut the door on them when they whine.

Beth would do anything she could think of to make you speak better and came up with lots of crazy ideas. My favorite was cooking. Beth would go out and buy boxes of food that needed to be cooked and as you cooked the food, she would make you read any words possible from the box, the recipe (yup, I learned that word from her and can say it pretty damn good if I do say so myself), our forks and spoons, plates, napkins and everything. She thought it was easier to learn to say things right if you had something to point to and could see the words as well, which she wrote down on a big blackboard. I think it was a great idea, cause I really liked cooking with her. I thought the stuff we made was complete shit, since I ate much better food at home and in restaurants. Except for the pizza mix–that was a pretty tasty one. I'm not sure any of it made my speech better, but we had fun and Beth was one of my favorites.

I remember the day my parents and I met with Beth to discuss my progress. My parents thought my speech was actually getting worse, not that they were blaming it on Beth or anyone. And my ear doctors in Philly over the years, there were two of them and they were both named Dr. Dave–great guys–had already told us that I had tiny ear canals and that they did fill up with crap and needed to be cleaned out a lot. By the way, I think all ear doctors are named Dr. Dave, cause my ear doctor in Tucson is also named Dr. Dave, and he is just as cool a dude as the other two Dr. Daves. Go figure. Anyway, Beth went through this big explanation about the program I was on and all sorts of stuff that I didn't understand. And I looked at my parents, who seemed OK with her explanation, until she finished with the line, "Sometimes you just have to get worse before you get better". Beth was cool and got along real good with my parents. My mom and dad just laughed and said, "Beth, you're full of shit." And then they all just burst out laughing and I did too, cause I didn't understand anything they said except that Beth was full of shit. I got that perfectly, and sometimes I would use that line on Beth during my speech therapy lessons, which she thought was hysterical. Hey, you work with what you got.

Chapter 6
Mr. C, Dr. B, and Kareem

OK, final apologies for lack of any other good stories from the first year. My bad.

But the next year, I moved into the big time. Room 107. Right after you walked in the front door of the school. The big man himself. Mr. Steve Curcio's class. When you first walk into Washington Elementary, you come to where two big hallways join right at the front door. Everyone came or went out that front door, so everyone ended up pretty much right in front of Mr. Curcio's classroom door at all times of the day. First thing in the morning, leaving at the end of the day and everything in between.

Just like any good street corner, the cool guys always hung out in the hallway right there. A lot–it was like a meeting place. I don't mean just the kids. I'm talking the cool teachers. So at the beginning and end of the day, you could always count on Mr. Curcio, Dr. Bradley, and Mr. B (Badaglicco–which I obviously can't say). Mr. B was beyond funny and I even went to his after school program for a while that he had set up in South Philly on Passyunk Ave, cause my parents said he was a good teacher and they wanted me to learn as much as I could. Mr. Curcio was there, too, which made it even more fun. Sort of like tutoring–and get this: Every student at that after school program got their own computer–no sharing. I actually learned a lot of important computer stuff at Mr. B's. I could have learned even more, except he had the hottest secretary I have ever seen in my life and I spent about half my time sitting with her and helping her out with her paperwork. She thought I was real cute, which worked out well for both of us. Mr. B and Mr. C would yell at me to get back to my computer, but I could blow them off for about a half hour at a time until I stayed with her too long. Eventually they would drag my ass back to the computer and I would start learning again. Anyway, back to the hall corner. Sometimes Sarah was around and maybe Rhoda (my next teacher's aide), and they were sorta members of the gang, too. They were all great and crazy people and I got some serious stories to tell about them.

Mr. Curcio was always in the hallway when the kids were getting to school in the morning, right near the front door of the school and was real friendly. He even used to say hi to me when I passed him in the hall my first year. And I would look in that room and see the older handicappers and they had all the maps and charts and kid's art all over the walls just like every other class. But they had one other thing that most of the classes did not. They had a computer. And I think a video game, because Mr. Curcio thought they were great ways to teach us. And he was right, too. They weren't easy to use like computers nowadays and didn't have all the great movies and wrestling and music and games on them like today, but you gotta start somewhere. In fact, they were black with green letters and the only games I remember were something called Pong (which I had played a bit in a bar in SF) and a weird version of Pac Man. But Mr. Curcio was real smart and knew this was going to be the future of all education. And he worked with me for years on getting better and better on computers until I actually became pretty good at them. He'd send things called floppy discs home with me to use on my home computer, along with my regular workbooks, and my mom and dad worked with me as well. He knew exactly what would interest me and what wouldn't. He's just a smart guy. Greatest teacher a guy could ever have. Now I know you don't want to hear about all my lessons in a special ed class, but some of them were really cool. Yeah, yeah, we did our numbers, reading words, learned a little history, and very academic stuff–but forget that. The best thing about Mr. Curcio was that he loved getting us out and about town. We used to go all around the neighborhood and sometimes rode a bus further away, so he could teach us about 'life'. They call this life skills, but that's just a fancy way to say learning how to make your way around town and just about anywhere in the world. We always went out around town at least one day a week and sometimes more. So we'd go to Burger King, bakeries, markets, bowling, Walmart, KMart, the 9th Street Market. You name any cool place around our school and we went there. And we learned how to order stuff and shop and use money and ride buses and everything. I knew a lot about some of this from my parents, but I learned a lot more from Mr. Curcio. My two favorite places to go were bowling and the 9th Street Market. The 9th Street Market is this whole long street where everyone is selling everything you could think of like fruits, vegetables, cheese, chicken, fish, pork, deli stuff, spices, fresh pasta, bakery stuff–everything you could possibly imagine. It's the street Rocky runs down in the first few Rocky movies, and when it was cold, they had big barrels with fires going to warm you up and for them to burn stuff in. The guys who worked there were crazy funny and some of them became friends since my dad and I shopped there every Saturday, along with Mr. Curcio and his kids, just for fun. And to buy our favorite foods and eat a bunch of stuff, cause there were great places to eat as well. I'll tell you some funny stuff about that later.

Bowling was the best, cause I was the best bowler. Most of the kids in my class sucked, so it made me feel pretty good being the best. I averaged about 150 a game at my peak later on, but in those days, I bowled a little above 100, which was pretty good. I don't want to give you the impression I knew what the hell I was doing, cause I bowled in a funny way, which I told you before. I would walk up to the line, spread my legs, and rock the bowling ball between my legs, and finally throw it down the lane using both hands – and NEVER with my fingers in the holes. It took about 10 seconds for the ball to hit the pins and the whole thing looked like it was a slow motion movie. I mean, sometimes, it looked like the ball would just stop and not even reach the pins. I think this happened a few times. But I got my scores fair and square, despite Carmen's arguments with me and everyone who was listening to him, including the owner of the bowling alley. See, Carmen could throw the ball real hard and looked just like the bowlers on TV. He looked just great at it. But half the time he threw gutter balls, so I beat his ass all the time. He claimed it was 'illegal' how I threw my ball, and that I was cheating. We argued about this every single time we bowled which was a lot, and everyone would just crack up. But the owner of the bowling alley checked the rulebooks and I was in the clear, so Carmen had to shut up and take his beatings like a man. I loved it.

Now my dad says I gotta do another one of those 'disclaimers'. He says my stories about Mr. Curcio are completely true and I am not making up anything, but I have to tell you that he became one of my family's best friends. And his whole family, too. His wife, Jeannie was the nicest person you could know, and the best Italian cook, and I had quite a few meals at their place that were mighty fine. She could really make me laugh. And I sort of grew up with his kids,

Paul and Julia, who are really cool. As I said, we spent many Saturday afternoons with them (starting a couple of years later), going food shopping and eating at the Italian Market on 9th Street, but I'll have more to say on that later–some pretty funny stories to come. When there was a really big wrestling event on pay-per-view, Steve and Jeannie would throw a party for me and Paul and Julia and friends and we would just yell and scream and eat and have a great old time at his house. We're all still great friends and talk on the phone and email all the time. Paul got married to a really nice woman and has two beautiful girls, and Julia is a writer. Much better than my dad, by the way. Every Christmas, Steve sends me a big tomato pie (it's a Philly thing–like a pizza without cheese–it's incredible–trust me). We are going on over 30 years of friendship here–that's a long time.

The kids in that class were great. Carmen was my best friend and my main man in class. We were what is known as mischievous–which I already explained to you earlier in the book. He had the strangest handicap I have ever seen, and it was only a couple of years ago that my dad finally figured out what it was, after watching a movie, no less. You see, Carmen's handicap was that he didn't seem to have a handicap at all! Carmen could talk up a storm. And he was something called 'social'. That means he could talk to anyone about anything and always got people to like him. Perfect speech–I mean he spoke just as well as any adult I ever met. Better than most, in fact. He was really a big help to me when people couldn't understand what I was saying. Carmen would set them straight in no time, even if he got it totally wrong. The perfect interpreter, because if he didn't understand me, he knew instinctively (that means he just knew without even thinking) what to say for me that would make the other person happy or like me more. That's a great talent. And EVERYONE liked Carmen. He was just the nicest, kindest and funniest guy you could ever want to know. My dad once asked Mr. Curcio why Carmen was in my class at all. And he said Carmen needed to be in the class. He had great language skills (fancy words for talking good), but he simply couldn't do much of the other stuff so well, like math and reading and even the computers and video games. Even I knew I was a little better at some stuff than Carmen. Turns out my dad and Steve (yeah, enough with the Mr. Curcio, I call him Steve now, but occasionally throw a Mr. Curcio at him for fun once in awhile) think Carmen has something called Williams Syndrome. Which has a few things like Down syndrome, especially the 'happy' gene, which is a great thing to have. It also made him cute. He looks like an elf–real stud. The Williams thing makes learning hard for him just like me, but he has this amazing skill at talking and communicating with people. And he has a special desire to want people to like him and can charm the pants off anyone. I'll give you an idea of how charming and persuasive Carmen became. He's had four children with four different girlfriends. He talked his way into a job as Security Staff at the Spectrum (that was like Philly's Madison Square Garden, but it's gone now), and it took them 2 weeks to figure out that he had no idea what he was supposed to do. He became a parking lot attendant for several weeks, despite not having a driver's license or really even knowing how to drive. He is now a part-time hockey coach, even though he can't skate and never played hockey in his life. Carmen is one of my heroes and I will always remember him as one of the best friends I ever had in school. Carmen could talk you out of your clothes for sure.

And I returned the favor for Carmen. I always helped him with his schoolwork when he needed it (not like I was some brain or anything), and taught him a lot about what I learned on the computer. See, we were each better in different things and we both knew that we could always count on each other to help the other guy out. That's what friends are for and as I already told you, Carmen was my best friend. But my other good friend in that class was Nate. Nate was probably harder to understand than me, but we got along great and had some good laughs together. Sometimes we didn't even know what the hell we were saying to each other, but somehow a feeling came across and we would smile and laugh. Nate had a great line he used at the end of every week on Friday afternoon. He learned it from Dr. Bradley, who was the gym teacher, basketball and other sports coach for the school, and probably the second most important guy in my entire school life, right after Mr. Curcio. Anyway, you might not have understood a lot of what I said or Nate said, but every Friday afternoon at the end of the day, there were often a lot of people gathering at that hallway corner. And Dr. Bradley would loudly ask Nate, "So what you doin' this weekend, Nate?" And Nate would respond in the most understandable line he could ever say, "Gonna get me $10, goin' to Atlantic City and gonna put it on red."

Now I know this doesn't sound that funny, but you had to be there. Nate had a great sense of comedic timing. I have been told the same thing, by the way. When Nate would say his line, everyone would just crack up (including him) at the thought of him riding a bus to play roulette at Atlantic City over the weekend. OK, maybe you had to be there. But it was fucking funny as hell and we did it every week for years. Nate was a classic.

Now Steve officially ran that class. He was the teacher after all. But as I said, he had a teacher's aide named Rhoda, who helped him out a lot. Steve had worked with Rhoda so long that he said she was just a second teacher since she knew how to do everything and he never really had to tell her anything. I liked Rhoda just as much as I liked Sarah from my last class, but they were different. Rhoda was quieter but just as funny. Real relaxed and mellow and would help you with anything at anytime. Your school work and learning, helping you get your boots and winter clothes on and off when you needed help, and was a pretty decent gamer for those days on the computer and video game system. I could usually beat her at most games, but admittedly, I needed her help to start up the computers, cause it wasn't so easy like today. Very complex stuff then. She thought I was funny and I thought she was cool. We became good friends for a lot of years. Rhoda had my back covered–always.

The other kids were real nice too. No crazies or scream-ers. Rita never talked at all and hardly ever smiled, but she was a nice girl. Helen was real big and could have beat the crap out of me, but she was not that sort of person–solid citizen. There were a few kids who came and went over the years that I didn't get to know as well as others, but it was a smooth ride. I didn't hang out with the girls much, since no boy in elementary school hangs out with girls much, except for the really big 8th grade normal guys, who hung out with some of the girls so much that they ended up having babies. But that wasn't really my crowd most of the time.

There were lots of great kids in my classes and the whole school, for that matter. But the fact remains, I would have been a special ed outcast if it wasn't for Dr. Bradley. Same for Carmen and Nate. But Dr. Bradley was a special guy. He was very well respected by all the teachers and especially by all the normal kids, because he was a take-no-shit sort of guy. As a coach, gym teacher and something called a disciplinarian. That meant if you started screwing around, he'd set you straight in a heartbeat. I might add that his basketball teams were damn good and I know for a fact that some of his kids went on to play college basketball. And a little later I'll tell you about an NBA player I met, who came from my school, too, though I don't know if Dr. Bradley was his coach or not. But the big kids in my school could play ball. Some of them could actually dunk in the 7th and 8th grade!!!

Well, as you can tell, Dr. Bradley really liked the special ed teachers and hung out with them on that hallway corner a lot. He was a member of that gang. But he also really liked the special ed kids, especially the funny guys that he called "characters". And you guessed it, he thought me, Carmen, and Nate were "characters". Which I guess means he just liked us and man, we liked him. So Dr. Bradley always made it a point to get us to hang out with him during the day. He would just drop by Mr. Curcio's class any time he felt like it and grab one of the three of us and walk the halls and talk with us, making sure every kid and teacher in that school knew we were friends of his, cause he never did that with the normal kids. Or he would take us to one of his gym classes and let us play with the normal kids. And since he was a tough guy, you bet your ass that none of the normal kids ever opened their mouths to complain that they had to take us on their team and stuff. His word was law. So after awhile, the three of us got 'reps'. That means reputations. And our reputations were that we were good guys and good friends of Dr. Bradley. And since no one was going to mess with Dr. Bradley, all the normal kids started treating us as normal too. And so did all the other teachers.

And there was this other thing that Dr. Bradley did that really made the three of us very important people. You see, Dr. Bradley often ran assembly in the auditorium each month. That was when the monthly awards were given out to all the students. Like 'Citizen of the Month', 'Most Improved Student', 'Student of the Month', 'Athlete of the Month' and that sort of stuff. You got ribbons and certificates. And me, Nate and Carmen would get an award of some kind every once in awhile, but not too much. No more than anyone else, I believe.

But what he did do was ALWAYS have one of the three of

us on stage standing right next to him when he announced the winners. And when people clapped and the winners came up on the stage, Dr. Bradley didn't give them their awards. He had us give the kids their awards from the table. That's right–every kid who got an award every month had it handed to them by me or Carmen or Nate, and had to shake our hands, which we were told to do, since that was the right thing when you give someone an important award. The first couple of times, the winners had funny looks, but like anything else, after awhile, everyone knew they were getting their awards directly from us and that really boosted us up the social scale (my dad's term).

The other person who helped me develop my 'rep' as a good guy at school was Kareem. He was one of the smartest and most sociable normal kids in the whole school. Almost everyone liked Kareem and if Kareem liked you, that went a long way towards everyone liking you. Now some of the really tough kids (like in gangs) didn't like Kareem cause they thought he was too smart and too good at school. Not a lot of kids, but a few. Sometimes they weren't nice to him and I'll tell you a little story about that. One time we went on a camping trip over a 3-day weekend, but it wasn't really a camping trip. It was a summer camp that had cabins to sleep in, not like the tents I was used to camping in. It was pretty easy–we had meals in a dining cabin, and you really didn't have to do any real camping stuff like collect firewood or go get water. But it was supposed to be a way for city kids to see the country. It was only for the normal kids, but Dr. Bradley and Mr. Curcio made sure Carmen and I got to go. They didn't leave Nate out, he just couldn't make it for some reason. And then the principal convinced my dad to be one of the adult supervisors, which is pretty funny since my dad has never even learned to be an adult to this day.

As soon as we got there, they split us into groups of ten or so to each cabin and Kareem and me, we got to be in the cabin my dad was watching–he got his own little side room and we all slept in bunks. Well, we all ran to a bunk and me and Kareem got bunks right next to each other so we could talk at night when we weren't supposed to. About 15 minutes after getting in the cabin, I was putting my boots on to go outside and like an idiot, I fell off the goddam bed and hit my head on the floor. OK, I'll admit it–it hurt–and I started to cry. Next thing you know, one of those big ass tough kids runs over and grabs Kareem by the neck and says, "I saw you push him over the bed, Kareem. I'm going to beat the shit out of you." Naturally, Kareem wasn't too happy at this and started screaming to let him alone, that he didn't touch me. Fortunately my dad could move faster in those days than he can now, and he was out in the room in a flash, breaking up the fight. He asked what happened and got the two different versions–the one with me falling off the bed and the one with Kareem knocking me over. My dad was pretty cool about it, checked me over and saw I was fine, and said, "I think this was an accident. Since no one else saw it, why don't we all just calm down and get our gear together and have a good time here. We don't have enough time to waste on fighting." The big kid again said that Kareem needed to pay for what he did and my dad just winked at Kareem and me and said, "Well, we'll keep an eye on everyone. How about that? And if I see anyone fighting or pushing anyone, I'm going to send them home immediately on one of the vans. Everyone clear on this?" And everyone nodded yes and that was that. The whole weekend, Kareem was by my side helping me out when I needed it, and I helped him out a couple of times too, cause frankly, I had done a whole lot more camping than he ever did. We had a great time, too.

So by being friends with Kareem, Dr. Bradley, and Mr. Curcio of course, I became "accepted" throughout the school, along with Carmen and Nate. We became friends with lots of normal kids and got to play on the playground and in other activities with normal kids, too. And since we were pretty fair athletes and funny guys and knew how to cuss as well as anyone, we stopped being stared at by anyone at all. And made some really nice friends. That changed my life in a lot of ways, as you can imagine. I can't really explain it, but it really made me feel good about myself.

Chapter 7
The Cupcake Song

It's time to tell the infamous Cupcake Story. I got into some deep shit over that. Minor race riot. Was not my fault at all. I will not accept any personal responsibility for it, since my heart was always in the right place. Just a small misunderstanding.

I liked music class a lot and I sung my heart out. My music teacher never actually told me I had any talent and I will admit I can't sing very well, but I can dance my ass off, and I have been on the Dancing Cam at University of Arizona sporting events in Tucson several times, so I have maintained my dancing skills. OK, I am delaying telling the story, so here it is. Judge for yourself and then let's move on.

One day, the music teacher taught us to play a singing game called the Cupcake Song. It's not a great song, you can't dance to it, and I didn't really like the music at all. But I liked the acting part of it. See, what you did was to sing a little bit about buying a cupcake, then you would pick out one of your classmates, sing something else that I think meant they were a cupcake, then they would sing some nonsense back to you. Then you would give them a make-believe quarter and buy them, since they were cupcakes, and they would go along back to your place in the class, since they were now your cupcake. It was sort of crazy, but I thought it was fun. I was a little kid, what the hell did I know. And this was a combined music class with mostly normal kids in it, because you wouldn't want to hear my special ed class try to sing a song together by themselves. Trust me.

I really liked that song and the game that went with it. So when I got home that afternoon, I told my mom I needed some quarters for school. She asked why and I told her that I needed to buy cupcakes. She asked if I had a note from Mr. Curcio, because usually when I needed to bring money to school, he would send a note home. But she didn't pay much attention and told me to get some from the change bowl where we all used to throw our spare change in, when our pockets had too many coins. I took eight quarters.

The next day I didn't have music class. I had play recess in the morning with a lot of the kids from my music class, though. And when I produced real quarters, their eyes got real wide. So we discussed the matter like adults, and it was agreed that if I gave each of them a quarter, they became my cupcakes and had to follow me everywhere on the playground, do everything I asked and even come back to my class and stand by my desk. And I didn't really ask them to do anything, in my defense. Just hang out with me and follow me around. So after recess, I went back to Room 107 with my eight cupcakes following me. Mr. Curcio asked what was up, and one of the kids said, "Shane bought us for a quarter and now we have to follow him around the rest of the day." Mr. Curcio laughed and sent them back to their own classes, but he wasn't laughing later that afternoon. Some of those kids went home for lunch and mentioned to their mom or dad what had happened. Only a slightly different story developed that some white kid bought 8 black slaves to follow him around, for a quarter apiece. Apparently, this is politically incorrect (my father's words). The exact details were explained to me when I was much older and could understand this. So that afternoon, there were 5 or 6 screaming mom's in the principal's office yelling about some racist thing that I didn't understand, and Mr. Curcio was called to the office to sort things out. Which took quite awhile and later, I saw the music teacher go in the principal's office, too, since her office was right across from Room 107. I heard a lot of yelling for a good while until things finally settled down. When Mr. Curcio came back, he was shaking his head, but I could see he was laughing as well. He pulled me over and told me to never bring any quarters or buy any cupcakes ever again. That was all he said. I later saw the principal, Judy, who liked me a lot, but she just shook her head and didn't smile at all. A couple of hours later, my mom came to pick me up and started to give Steve a hard time about not telling her I needed quarters. And he laughed and said, "Don't go there". And explained what happened. My mom started laughing so hard, I thought she was going to pee in her pants and even Steve started laughing again. And he said, "Don't even look at Judy. She's not laughing and she's the one who has to deal with the parents."

Naturally, the whole thing blew over after a couple of days and all was forgotten, at least I think it was forgotten. But you can bet your ass, the Cupcake song was never played in music class ever again in the history of that school.

And to this day, when I want to make my parents laugh, I sometimes start to sing them the Cupcake Song.

Chapter 8
The Building, Jesse, Meatball, and Angela

While all this school stuff was happening, a whole bunch of other stuff was going on too. We finally found a house and that house is a story of its own. By the time I got to Steve's class, my parents finally found a permanent place for us to live in, right in the middle of Old City in Philadelphia, just a block from where our loft was. Old City is a real tourist attraction now and has fancy restaurants, cafes and art galleries. Back then it had mostly warehouses, like our neighbors who were something called shoe wholesalers, a bunch of kitchen supply stores, and even a ladder company. Daytime the streets were mostly filled with trucks getting loaded and nighttime, there was hardly ever anyone on the streets. My parents loved that. My dad wrote those last sentences by himself–but I am officially verifying them as accurate, cause it really was a cool neighborhood. Ben Franklin's house and Betsy Ross' house are there. So are the Liberty Bell and Independence Hall, and other history places. But it just wasn't as crowded as it is now. This was my new backyard and it was great. But our new house wasn't a house. It was this gigantic building called a warehouse. It wasn't like Jerry's warehouse in SF–it was real narrow and long and tall–4 floors. I'm told it was about 10,000 square feet, which means nothing to me except it was big. I liked it when I first saw it, until (once again) I went inside. The place was crumbling just like our first house in that crappy town on the Main Line, which we finally got rid of. But the reason it was crumbling was because it was built in 1760. Yup, older than the USA. In the front part, it had a big winch and rope that went from the top floor all the way to the basement, with a trap door on every floor. Talk about some great rides up and down the whole building–though I always had to ride with an adult. When my dad and mom bought the building, they got a hospital along with it. The first floor was occupied by a guy named Jesse, whose business was called The Handbag Hospital. He fixed things made out of leather, so it really wasn't a hospital for people. Now Jesse wasn't much of a talkative guy at first. In fact, he really wouldn't talk to any of us at all when we first moved in. My dad had already told him he could stay in his store for as long as he wanted, which seemed to please him a little but my dad said he just didn't trust us for some reason. He was an older black gentleman with a very young daughter about my age, who was very nice and later would sometimes come over to play with me. Jesse later became a real good friend of ours and we fooled around all the time. It just took him a good year or so to warm up to us. How good a friend? Well here's a quick story for you, a few years later. One time my dad had to go away for some medical conference for a week and asked Jesse to keep an eye on things, and specifically my mom and me. That night my mom happened to look out the front window of our upstairs living area and noticed that Jesse's lights were shining onto the street at around 10 o'clock just before I was going to hit the hay, which was very strange. So we went down to turn the lights off and found Jesse sleeping on an old couch he had in his store, with an old revolver on his chest. Just snoring away. So she woke him up and fortunately he didn't panic and shoot her. My mom asked him what the hell he was doing sleeping in the store and why the hell he had a gun. Jesse got this serious look on his face and said, "Bob asked me to keep an eye on you two and the building, so I'm staying here for the nights as well." It took my mom a good 15 minutes to convince Jesse to go home and that we were OK, but Jesse said he needed to hear it from my dad, who called him the next day to tell him he should stay at home at night. How many of your friends would do that for you? Jesse was as solid as they come. But I tell you, he was a real tough guy, a son-of-a-bitch, according to other people in the neighborhood. But my dad says he just didn't take shit from anyone. Not a bad guy at all–in fact, my dad also says he was the most honest guy in all of Old City. Just someone you didn't mess with. He was friends with lots of cops in Philly cause he repaired all their leather holsters. Gave me a couple of old ones for myself a few times, too and I loved wearing them. He'd introduce cops to me when I happened to hang in his store once in awhile and they were all super. They'd show me their badges and even their guns, though I wasn't allowed to touch. Jesse always watched over me, especially later when I had some jobs in the neighborhood. He would always watch me walk down the sidewalk when I left and look for me when I got back, to make sure no one messed with me. He didn't need to, cause no one ever bothered me at all–it was a real friendly neighborhood and almost every storeowner knew me after awhile and they all looked out after me. So did all my police friends when they were around. For no particular reason that I can think of.

Our building was huge, but was missing a few things. Like a kitchen–just a hot plate and an old little sink where the kitchen was supposed to be. That's because the owner, Ron, and his girlfriend Angela were starving artists and couldn't fix the place up even though they loved it. But Ron was a great photographer and had a professional darkroom, which my parents really liked. And a sauna on the roof that he built himself. So there was good stuff and bad stuff about the place. It took about 3 years of constant construction to return the place to its original look and fix it up right, and we lived through it every day, but it was fun. Dave Abel was the best historical restoration (no clue about that) guy in like the whole US and he became a great friend to all of us over those three years. So did his crew. They were there so long that one guy met a girl in one of the lunch places down the street, married her and had 3 kids–all because he was in our house for 3 years. Dave's dog, Buster could walk on our really slanted front roof with no trouble at all and no human being other than Dave ever walked on that roof without a rope on 'em. It was sort of a circus for a long time, and my dad says he has never heard of anyone having a construction crew in their house that long and everyone still be best friends at the end. Dave even came out to visit us for a couple of weeks in Tucson for vacation years later, cause we always kept in touch with him.

Ron and Angela hated having to sell the place, but it turned out they came over to see it a lot, because they became best friends with us. I hear that's a strange thing to happen as well–become friends with the people you buy your house from. Our friendship really started only a few days after we moved in. They sold my dad a big heavy wooden dresser, mostly because it was too heavy to move and no one wanted to be bothered with it, neither Ron or my dad. I was playing around on it and then I opened one of the big drawers and it was full of thousands of pennies, so I showed my dad. He called them. Now Ron, who I later nicknamed "Meatball", a name that stuck with us to this day, was from the South and had a real thick drawl–sometimes I couldn't even understand him, though he wasn't handicapped to my knowledge. And Angela was from Puerto Rico and had a thick Spanish accent and I had a little trouble with her speaking as well. We got Angela on the phone and my dad told her she should stop by because she had left a whole bunch of pennies in the dresser. She literally squealed out loud and apologized about 10 times and told us she was so embarrassed and would be right over. Which we all thought was pretty strange. I mean, who really cares about pennies? So about an hour later, Meatball and Angela arrived and she had a little suitcase that she said she was going to put them in, which seemed stranger than her squeal. We watched her go over to the dresser and open the drawers and she turned around and said, "I'm sorry, but I don't see them." She really looked embarrassed even worse. So I walked over and opened the penny drawer and pointed. She looked for a second and screamed again and her face became so red, it looked like an apple. Finally, she said, "Oh my god, I'm so sorry. I thought you said I left a drawer full of my 'panties'." I think it happened because of her thick Spanish accent. And then everyone cracked up and we sat down and started to talk. Then we found out they liked dominoes like me, and the beers came out, we all played (I was Angela's partner) and that's how we became best friends. Angela was my first real crush. I loved Angela and still do to this day. I always sat on her lap or next to her and she was always so affectionate to me. Except at Phillies games. You don't ever want to sit next to Angela at a Phillies game. Because she is what my dad calls, "an insane, hot-blooded, Latino baseball fanatic". Any time anything went bad for the Phillies during a game, she would yell or scream something and punch the person next to her in the arm or grab their arm and dig her nails into it. The Meatball wouldn't sit next to her at the games and neither would my mom. I tried but it was too painful. Which left my dad, who came home from every game black and blue.

Meatball and Angela bought me the very first version of Grand Theft Auto, a pretty cool video game. We all sat down to watch me try it out, cause they all sucked at video games and I was the best. So it started out and they and my parents were really getting into watching and yelling stuff at me like, "Shano, pick up the chain and keep beating him until he's dead", and "Get the knife, man, stab that guy in the chest till he drops", as well as, "go get the prostitute and take her in the building." After a few minutes, my mom and Angela looked at each other and started laughing and they said, "What the hell are we saying to him? Maybe this game is a little much for Shano at his age." "Nonsense," said The Meatball and my dad. And that's how I became good at Grand Theft Auto. I didn't understand the game very much, but I had good game skills so I could do what they told me. And it was sort of fun beating up people, but I moved on in later years to mostly sports video games.

Chapter 9
The Building, Thanksgiving, and the Philadelphia Police

Eventually, the building was finished and man, that was the greatest house a kid could live in. My bedroom had three different levels, so you could arrange mattresses and pillows and jump from one level down to the next and then the next–it was great. My ceiling was 22 feet high and I had an almost regulation basketball hoop in there. Floor to ceiling windows where I could watch fireworks on the Delaware River on New Year's Day and July 4th, though we usually watched from the roof. My dad says my room was about 1,000 square feet, which I'm telling you is pretty damn big. I also used my parent's bedroom in another part of the place and that was like 2000 sq ft and get this, we had a second kitchen in there cause it came with an old cast iron stove and sink when we bought it (it was an apartment then) and it was easy to just put another kitchen in there. Which was a good idea cause later we had Monica, my 'social companion' live on the second floor there for several years, and I hung out in that place a lot with her. Monica was a great friend and we had great times cruising around Old City, going to movies and eating out. Cause sometimes you just don't want to always be with your parents and my parents knew that, so they made sure I had times where I could go out with my own friends, and not just like organized activities like Special Olympics or rec centers. Monica had some pretty cool friends, too—some very fine women. We partied hard.

My other great 'social companion' (silly word for a friend) was Lil, who still comes out to visit us in Tucson to this day. She and I also went everywhere, all over Philly, just like Monica. They both didn't take crap from anyone and always made sure I had good seats at stuff so I could see, and brought me over to hang out with their friends, and go to parties. We three have some pretty funny stories to tell, too. But some of them would piss my parents off, cause we got wild sometimes, so I promised to keep them secret. I can't get them in trouble. Sorry.

Anyway, I didn't use my parent's bedroom (when Monica wasn't living there) for the kitchen but because my dad had about 4 or 5 real pinball machines in there for his own amusement. He thought he was quite the player and admittedly, he could kick everyone's ass, but that's only because he had been playing it since college and he got real good on his machines. I saw him play in bars sometimes and he won a lot, but I saw a few people kick his butt, too, so he wasn't that great. I remember this one bar we were at where I was playing by myself for a while. My mom and dad were pretty far away at our table. This really hot babe came up to me and asked if she could play and we played a couple of games. I'm no expert, but I'm fairly certain she was drunker than any person I had ever seen before in my life. Could barely stand up and in fact, she kept her arms around me almost the whole time so she could stand up. And I kicked her butt in pinball. Then she asked where I was sitting and I brought her over to meet my parents. She was very affectionate and kissed me a couple of times, but

I was getting a little turned off, cause she was drooling a bit–very wet kisses. So she walked up to my parents and plopped down in a chair and said, "Shane is such a great guy. How long have you known him?" My parents did the eye rolling thing and my mom said, "Since the day he was born." And the girl said, "Wow! That's a long time." Needless to say, my parents were not impressed with my pickup, and my dad escorted her back to the bar where he found her friends to help her. He says she asked for my phone number and he just laughed and gave her a fake one. That sort of pissed me off, but I have to admit I don't like hanging out with drunk people.

But lots of people and kids came over to our building all the time to play, so we had many ongoing little tournaments of pinball. Those games made me lots of new friends as well. I got pretty good, but not great. There was no shortage of fun in that building and we lived there for over 10 years.

Just like in SF, my mom loved to have big Thanksgiving and holiday parties, but now we had real space, so the place would get filled with people. Sometimes like almost a hundred people, all friends. And everyone was assigned to bring something to eat, though my mom and dad would always get some special stuff like a whole roast pig from Cannuli's House of Pork that took two people to carry on a big wooden board or sometimes pigs from Chinatown, or my mom would roast a bunch of birds to eat. Everyone brought great food and it started around noon and ended around 2 am. People would go down to the second floor and take naps and rest so they could come back to the 3rd floor and start eating again. One time, everyone was just stuffed and unable to get up out of their chairs or off the couches around 9 o'clock. Just tuckered out. Suddenly, my dad's buddy, Doan, from Vietnam, arrived with his whole family as well as another Vietnamese family and they came with another whole Thanksgiving dinner, Vietnamese-style.

I'm talking a complete Vietnamese dinner for like 50 people and some weird looking stuff, too. I wouldn't touch it. No one had the heart to say they were stuffed, so everyone just got back up and started eating again. I think a few people got sick just from eating too much. But man, Gwen (Doan's wife) made this huge bowl of shrimp and that was gone in about 10 minutes. A bunch of people just passed out after midnight and in the morning there were about a dozen people sleeping around the building in different places–they just couldn't make it home.

A few days earlier there had been an argument and a potential fight over food assignments, but not really. See, we were good friends with the best bakery guys in Philadelphia, which was in Old City–it was called 'Au Fin Palais'. Don't take my word for it–it was always named best dessert bakery in Philly in Philadelphia Magazine and run by my good friend Pascal, the owner, who was from France, and his partner, Freddie, who was from Puerto Rico, just like Angela (who made great cranberry sauce). They were gay– and I have lots of gay friends, which I still don't understand completely except that they really loved each other–really solid guys–I mean the best. But they seemed to argue and scream at each other most of the time. In different languages so they couldn't understand each other when they cussed. I learned a little cussing in both French and Spanish, which is useful, I think. When they got real busy, sometimes they would call my mom and me to come over and help out. I mostly ate any bread product I could get my hands on and watched, but my mom is a good baker and she really did help them out–just for the fun of it. Anyway, when the food assignments came out for Thanksgiving, Morris got assigned the main desserts, cause his hobby was baking, he was an incredible baker, and he had been making the desserts for several years. And this was Pascal's and Freddie's first Thanksgiving with us. So Pascal and Freddie got assigned the appetizers cause anything they made was great, especially things called quiches and little 'hors d'oeuvres' which I think is the French word for tasty tiny things to eat. Well, Pascal went nuts and was very insulted. I mean so insulted that he threatened not to come. My mom and dad tried to calm him down at his bakery but he would not calm down at all. Just got madder and madder–my mom said it was the 'French' in him. So finally, my dad said he'd bring Morris by and they could discuss sharing the dessert duties. Next day or so, he and Morris dropped by and things changed a bit. I think I already told you that Morris was an NCAA Heavyweight Wrestling champion when he was in college, but he also would have been in the real Olympics if he hadn't gotten injured, and he won the World Silver Medal in Sambo Wrestling one year in Moscow, which is a sport that combines judo and wrestling–I watched him compete once in my life and he kicked the shit out of everyone who came near him. Did I mention that Morris is 6'1" and 310 pounds and is one of the meanest looking black dudes you will ever see? Which is really very funny, cause he is a teddy bear–after all his hobby is baking, and he is Dr. Morris Johnson, a child psychologist who helps kids who aren't happy. His wife was Ellen, my dad's piano teacher, who was so tiny compared to Morris, it was hysterical to watch them walk together. But she was a very big composer and had her music played around the world sometimes by whole orchestras. Anyway, even though Morris was a teddy bear, I still wouldn't want to piss him off. Very quickly, he and Pascal became friends and for some odd reason, Pascal said he was very happy to make the appetizers. Which were fantastic, as were Morris' desserts.

Wrapping up that Thanksgiving, I must add that it was the first time I ever got drunk. By accident, mind you. Pascal's dad was visiting from France and he brought a bottle of homemade Calvados for the party. I had no clue what it was and still don't, but Pascal poured me a small amount in a glass to sip and I smelled it and immediately knew it was apple juice, which at the time was my favorite drink. So I grabbed the bottle, filled the glass and chugged the whole glass without even thinking. No adult was really paying that much attention to me–it was a party man, I had my own friends to hang with, especially my 'brother', Matt. Boy, did my mouth burn!!! I had my face under the faucet for a couple of minutes. A few minutes later I was laughing my ass off, then I couldn't stand any more, and last thing I remember I was put in bed. I came alive a few hours later, but never really figured out what happened till I started doing tequila shots in Tucson years later.

One more building story. It got me in big trouble. I mean big trouble. I was in the school nurse's office one day for some minor thing I can't remember, but she was sorta strange and I liked babbling to her nonstop, cause I knew I could confuse the hell out of her. Just screwing around with her. And I simply mentioned that my parents locked me in a cage every night when we all went to bed. Said it pretty clearly too. She made me repeat it several times and she repeated it back to me several times, so after all that practicing, I could say it very clearly. Anyone could understand me. Then later in the day, I was called back to her office and there was another lady there with her and they asked me to repeat it. And I again said that when we went to sleep at night, my parents locked me in a cage. They had a real funny look on their faces and they examined me all over for god knows what. Then they sent me back to class.

After I got home, around 6 o'clock, the doorbell rang. Now you have to understand, we spent most of our time on the third floor, and the stairs from the ground to the third floor were pretty steep and hard to climb. So there was an intercom to talk to anyone ringing the bell, since we couldn't see them. And when my dad asked who was there, they answered, "Philadelphia Police and Child Welfare Services. Could you please come down, sir?"

I have to admit, I made no connection with the school nurse, who apparently called some other folks about my cage remark. My dad went down there and according to his version, they repeated my remarks and said they would have to come in and inspect our whole building and talk to me. My dad didn't have much choice but kept saying the whole thing made no sense. He wasn't angry (yet) or pissed, but seemed confused. So these two cops and two other ladies walked all around the building and though they found it rather odd ('unconventional' say my parents), they were mighty impressed when they came into my room and I was watching TV in a hammock hanging over my bed, while shooting Nerf basketballs. And they couldn't find any cage. They even went into the basement, which was so scary to me that I only went in it once the whole time I lived there. So finally they brought me into the dining area, sat me down and asked me to repeat what I said, right in front of my parents. And I'm a man of truth, so I said, "Yes, when we go to sleep, my dad locks us in a cage." No one noticed that I now said 'us' and not 'me'. My parents looked at me like I was nuts and my dad started to say something, but one of the cops politely told him to shut up, and asked me to show him the cage. I said sure and led everyone down the stairs to the ground floor at the entrance of the building. See, we had a regular front door with a nice glass window and everything, but since just the three of us were living in that building (except when Monica was with us), and our space was so high up and far away from that door, you couldn't hear a goddam thing if someone was trying to break the glass or break in the door or anything like that. It was just too far away. So my parents had Dave install a door made of iron bars (like a jail cell door) just before you got to the stairs–that created a little room between the wood/glass front door and the iron barred door. You could leave your wet boots and stuff there. During the daytime that iron bar door was always open and flat against the wall, because as I have already told you, it was a busy street and no one was going to try to break it down in broad daylight. And Jesse would have beat the shit out of them or shot 'em anyway. But just before we went to bed, my dad would go down the stairs and lock the iron bar door until morning for safety. Thus, technically, I was absolutely correct–my parents did, in fact lock me in a cage every night. I just neglected to mention they locked themselves in the same cage and that the cage was about 10,000 square feet in size–the entire building. The cops laughed, the ladies smirked (that's when you sort of laugh but act like you're better than someone), and my dad pretended to smile, but I knew he was mighty pissed.

The good news is that I didn't get a time out or any punishment like no TV or video games or wrestling for a while or anything like that. In fact, I didn't even get yelled at. They sat me down and pretty much just said, "Don't do that shit ever again". Because they knew that I knew I was being 'mischievous'. I got the message, and I never did that sort of shit ever again.

Chapter 10
Employment and funny bosses

One day, my dad and I went around the corner to the Mulberry Market, which was the only little grocery store near us, to get a few things. And my dad and the owner, Diane (a great lady) started chatting. Diane thought I was just the cutest and funniest guy in the world, and I could go in there anytime I wanted and get stuff by myself and my mom or dad would just pay her later if I didn't happen to have enough money on me. It was real easy to get there, cause I didn't even have to cross any streets, which sometimes got busy with all the buses, cars and trucks. And horses with carriages that the tourists rode. My mom and I got to know lots of the horse and carriage folks, and when they were empty and passed us on the street, they would yell for me and we would jump on and get a lift for a few blocks wherever we were going. I thought I was in a western movie, it was so cool.

Anyway, on this trip to the Market, all of a sudden, Diane asks us if I wanted a part-time job there. My dad was kinda surprised, but I thought it was a great idea. Just a few hours a day on weekends, though later I did a few hours lots of days during the week, when I wasn't in school. So we went home and talked it over as a family and it was a unanimous vote, and I finally got my first job.

It was a sweet job too. I have no idea how much money I made, but they always gave me some cash at the end of my shift, which I brought home and kept in a jar in my room, until I would spend it on crap I happened to see when I was out. I also loved buying rounds of drinks whenever we were in bars with friends and I pissed away a lot of money on that simply cause it made me feel good. I really didn't care much about the money, cause whenever I needed money, my parents gave me some. It's not like I asked them to buy me a car or anything. I always had pocket money. The job was very interesting, too. I had lots of things to do like sweep, break down cardboard boxes (I loved stomping on them), put stuff on the shelves (that's called a stock boy), and fairly quickly, I was even promoted to Director of the Dairy Case.

Now the Dairy Case wasn't just the Dairy Case. It had milk, yogurt, butter, margarine, cream cheese, half and half and all the things that are called dairy. But it had all the other things that needed to be in a fridge, too, cause this wasn't like a supermarket. There were cold juices, lemonade, and weird stuff like packages of smoked salmon or pickled herring. I couldn't read all the labels, but I'm pretty smart and it took me no time at all to recognize all the different things and know exactly where they were supposed to be. So when I arrived at work (this was later on after I became an expert at the dairy case), the first thing I would do was straighten out the goddam dairy case, because it was always a fucking mess. Not because of the Market folks, but because customers would move stuff around to reach for something they wanted and never put things back the way they were supposed to be. So the juices would get mixed with the yogurt, the jars of smoked fish would end up next to the milk and so forth. Drove me crazy. So for the first few weeks as Director of the Dairy Case, I never let that case get out of my sight if at all possible. I'd carefully watch each and every person who opened it and took something out. And if they moved stuff around and didn't put everything back properly, I'd run over immediately and start showing them what they did wrong and how to put everything that they moved back in the correct place. They would look at me like I was crazy, but you can bet your ass I made them straighten things out, cause I had better things to do than teach them how to use the dairy case. Occasionally, someone would try to ignore me and walk away, but I would run up to Diane or Jane (she was a great friend and manager of the store) and rat them out as messing up the case. Everyone else thought I was joking around and laughed, but I think people should be very considerate and keep things neat. And though I think it became a bit of a joke for all the other employees, our customers soon learned not to fuck with my dairy case.

Back to my first day at work. It was very exciting that first day. The weather was perfect–it was a beautiful, warm spring day and when I got there, Diane and Jane gave me my own perfectly white shopkeeper's apron and helped me put it over my head and tie it on. I looked like the damn boss of the place. Then they gave me a broom and said my first task was to sweep the sidewalk. That was absolutely the best part of my job! You see, my dad says I am a 'schmoozer'–that means I like to talk to just about anyone who comes near me. And out on the sidewalk with my big broom, I got to see tons of people. Lots of neighborhood friends and acquaintances and other people including complete strangers would walk by and stop to chat with me all the time. Normally, it took most people about 5 minutes to sweep the front sidewalk, but everyone knew it took me about 30 minutes, cause I had to socialize for the other 25 minutes. And I think I drummed up some business for them, since after talking with me for awhile, lots of people would remember they needed something at the market and end up going inside to buy stuff. Sweeping the sidewalk on a sunny day is just a great way to spend an afternoon.

Course, my FIRST day sweeping the sidewalk didn't go very smoothly, because my bosses didn't take the time to explain to me exactly what they wanted me to do. I mean, when you have new people working, you gotta explain exactly what needs to be done. How else can you run a business? They just gave me a broom and said sweep the sidewalk. That's not a lot of detail. As the story goes, about 30 minutes later, someone came out to get me and I was gone. They looked up and down the street and I was nowhere to be seen. Apparently they panicked and called my mom and dad who came running over and they couldn't find me either. They looked in the basement, in the upstairs storage areas, in the back by the dumpster, everywhere. I was just gone. I wasn't there to see, but I bet my mom was crying, cause she probably thought I was going to end up with my picture on a milk carton–I loved those pictures of kids and always wondered what I needed to do to get on them–though I learned about that later and that's not really a good thing.

Well, what happened was that I didn't know exactly how much sidewalk to sweep. And I already knew lots of the storeowners around that whole city block. So when I finished the Market sidewalk, I started sweeping the sidewalk next door and that guy knew me (I think it was the cleaners) and came out and thanked me and gave me a buck. This seemed like a good gig and as I said, it was a beautiful day to be outside. So I kept working my way down Arch Street, sometimes getting a thank you, or a buck, or even nothing at all except the fun of sweeping. Then I turned the corner to go down 2nd Street. Same thing–lots of stores, friends, and sweeping and I was having a ball until I was pretty much out of sight. And I really got out of sight when I reached all the way to Market Street and made another right turn. Well, they put out a local search party, but it wasn't until my mom went home to wait by the phone that they located me. I was sweeping the sidewalk on Market Street in front of the Magic Shop, and that guy was a buddy of mine and we talked a bit. He wanted to know why I was all the way over there sweeping his sidewalk with an apron on, but he couldn't understand what I was telling him. So he called my mom and they finally came to get me. I protested a bit, because I wanted to finish the whole block, all four blocks without crossing the street, but it was getting a little dark and cool, so I gave in. Everybody thought it was the funniest thing in the world, but I thought I was just doing a damn good job. Next day when I swept, Jane made sure to show me exactly where to start and stop and didn't take her eye off me the whole time. I adapted.

Jane was my real job coach and taught me everything I had to do. I won't bore you with shopkeeping talk, but I had to learn a lot of stuff and she was a great teacher and it was a great job. She became one of my best friends and we would take breaks and lunch together and talk about my favorite wrestlers and everything about Philly sports teams. Jane was the best.

About 2 weeks after I started my job at the market, we were all having dinner at Charlie's restaurant, which was just around the block and across the street. It was called 'Something Special', and he made something called Middle Eastern food, which is not something I particularly cared for, but that didn't really matter, cause Charlie would make me anything I wanted even if it wasn't on the menu. If I wanted hot dogs or cheese sandwiches, they would magically appear. Later, he turned the place into a bar, called Charlie's Place, which I liked better, cause he had pool tables then, and I'm a pretty decent pool player. In fact, when I played pool at Charlie's, I never had to pay for my time at the table. That became known to everyone very quickly, so almost everyone wanted to play pool with me, all the time. I had no problem getting players, when it became a bar.

Anyway, Charlie and his wife Debbie ran that place (along with their fabulously beautiful daughters, all of whom I love, especially Esther) and they were all from some place called Israel. Debbie is the sweetest lady in the world, which makes it hard to understand how Charlie was so lucky to have her. Because even though Charlie is and will always be one of my best friends ever in my whole life, he's pretty crazy. Funny crazy, but crazy all the same. He is a really big guy–taller than Morris and almost as wide and talks loud, and tells stories non-stop, most of which I can't understand, but he can make anyone laugh when he wants to. He can also piss off anyone he wants to.

So we start telling Charlie about my new job and all of a sudden, he starts getting pissed. "You got Shane a job at another place without asking me? Why didn't you talk to me? I could use a man like Shane right here. Now I'm insulted." And he went back to the kitchen. Wouldn't come out and sit with us like he usually did. Charlie was what my mom called 'a little dramatic'; he took everything personally and acted insulted all the time. But in a funny way–cause he was sort of a comedian too. Finally, we talked to Debbie and got him back at the table and he said, "Unless Shane comes to work for me too, I will be insulted for the rest of my life."

So in just two weeks, I had 2 jobs, after years of unemployment. Now working at Charlie's was very different from the Market. I had big responsibilities at the Market–that was serious work. At Charlie's, I was a busboy and part-time waiter. I worked in the afternoons–that was the slow time–not that many customers until dinner and I was done by then. So I cleared some tables and brought some dishes to people (most of whom I knew), though I couldn't take orders since I couldn't write very well. And I passed out drinks and stuff. But there was a lot of slow time and that's when Charlie and I would get into it. I'd sit down when there was nothing much to do and ask for lunch or a snack and Charlie would make me something to eat. After I was done, he would come by my table and tell me to sweep or clear some tables or stock some shelves in the back. Since I always thought of Charlie as part of my family, I didn't feel particularly pressured to impress him–he was like a having an uncle around. So I felt it perfectly fine to sometimes refuse to do what he asked, cause it was fun to watch him get pissed off. I knew he wasn't really pissed off–he was really just acting and so was I. So we gradually developed a routine where he would give me something to eat and once I had my fill, I would generally refuse to work for about a half hour, in order to relax and digest my food. Charlie would act pissed and say he had no time for a lazy bum like me and he wasn't going to pay me. Then he would fire me and send me home. I'd go home and tell my mom and dad I got fired, they would smile and dial Charlie and put me on the phone and I would apologize and beg for my job back, which I always got. A couple of times I got scared and thought he really did fire me and I cried once or twice and really did beg for my job back, but he would always laugh and take me back. Sometimes we would reverse the routine. That's when I would finish eating (no matter what happened, I always made sure I got my food eaten first), and when Charlie asked me to do something, I would take off my apron (yup, I had a cool apron there too), throw it in his face and tell him I quit and walk home. Then he would call my house and beg for me to come back and after a few minutes, I would agree to return if he made me more food, which he always did. Man, it was fun working at Charlie's. And eating at Charlie's too–cause he was a great cook and had huge portions. Whenever we ate there, he wouldn't let my dad eat anything on the menu–he would always say, "Forget the menu. I'm going to make you something so good, that you will never want to eat anything else again." The he'd come back with a plate with about 5 pounds of food on it that my dad always loved, but which he couldn't ever finish. That's when Charlie would come back, look at the food left on my dad's plate, and say, "Why do I bother with you? You don't like my food. You won't even finish one plate." And he would walk off in a huff. And we would all crack up laughing.

The other restaurant I hung out at all the time was Old City Pizza. Right on the corner at the end of our block. It was owned by Pat and Leo, whose daughter Sue (Sula was her real first name) was married to John and they all worked there to run the place. Along with George and one of their sons, Alex. And their younger kids used to come and hang out too. And the gorgeous blonde bombshell, Vasso, who was John's sister–one of my all-time favorite crushes. They weren't from Israel–they were from Greece. You get the picture–it was a crazy place run by a whole bunch of Greeks and they can be the funniest people in the world. I never had a job there, but sometimes when they got real busy like when a tour bus arrived to look at the Liberty Bell down the street, they would frantically call my mom and dad to help out–my mom would be a waitress and my dad was the soda jerk–we just called him the jerk for short–that got a big laugh. Only for a few hours, but my parents loved it because they really liked that whole family. I would clear a few tables but mostly hung right next to John, who was the chief cook. John was one of the best friends I ever had. I know I keep saying everyone was my best friend and they really were but some people like John and Charlie were just extra special. We became good friends and on Greek Easter we would go to their house and, get this, they would kill a real live goat in their backyard and roast it in a pit in the ground and make a whole feast. I loved the whole thing–Greek music, dancing, drinking and laughing. These people knew how to throw a party.

My parents said Pat made the best split pea soup ever invented. I thought John made the best pizza ever invented, but everyone else wouldn't even take a bite of it. John knew I had soft teeth and couldn't chew on hard stuff, so he would make me a special pizza that was only half cooked and it became one of my all time favorite meals. But after a couple of times, they said I had to eat it away from the windows and front door, cause when people looked in the windows and saw a half cooked pizza that had white crust, apparently that wasn't good for business.

Chapter 11
The Playground and the Judge

A few years later, one cold night, my dad got a call from Diane's husband, Dick. And then we all had to go over to their house nearby and they all had a long talk that I didn't know much about since I was watching TV. They all looked pretty bummed out. But the next day at the Market, Jane wasn't there, and the next day, and then the whole week. 2 weeks. I knew something was up and I got a little worried and kept asking everyone where Jane was, but no one would tell me a damn thing.

Finally my dad sat me down and half-ass explained something to me that I really didn't get, except for the general principal of the thing. See, many years before when Jane was very young, she had got in trouble for smoking those funny smelling cigarettes called marijuana. I know about marijuana cause I got to vote on it in Arizona a few years ago to make it a medicine for some people. I can't tell you how I voted cause that is a secret–that's why they call it a secret ballot. Anyway, Jane got in trouble once and ran away from that trouble and now the police had come to see her and she was going to have to go to court, just like

Judge Judy. And my dad said she might have to go to jail cause running away from the court is apparently a bigger deal than smoking marijuana. I don't get that at all, but that's the story I got.

My dad made all sorts of phone calls that week and I heard a lot of them, but it didn't mean much to me what he was saying. I just wanted Jane back–she was my friend. But this one night, he wrote a long letter to a guy called the prosecutor who was the lawyer who was trying to send Jane to jail–I've seen those guys on TV lots of times. And my dad showed me the letter and told me it was all about how Jane had done so much to help me be a better person, that she was my friend and teacher (job coach, that is), and that because of this, she was now a better person and shouldn't go to jail at all.

About a week later, that guy called my dad at night and asked if the letter was true. I've already told you my dad is considered one of the world's great bullshitters. But this letter was so convincing that the guy said his wife cried when she read it. My dad swore it was all true and that Jane was an amazing person who had a tremendous effect on me as a person, which WAS completely true. No bullshit this time. And that guy said he was something called 'sympathetic' towards Jane, and would do his best to help her, but that the Judge wasn't Judge Judy. He was a guy known as a 'hanging judge'. That means he wasn't sympathetic and the prosecutor said he wasn't very optimistic about Jane staying out of jail for a while.

So a week later, my mom and me headed out with Dick and Diane for a real long ride somewhere in New Jersey (my dad had to work at the hospital) and we got to this really cool group of big buildings in the middle of nowhere. And outside, there's this big playground with a really tall fence around it and something my mom called 'barbed wire'. And a whole bunch of guys wearing orange uniforms on both teams were playing full court basketball and man, they could play ball. I begged to go play, but my mom gave me the 'shut up' look and I shut up pretty quick.

Next thing you know we're in a courtroom just like on TV, and this real mean looking judge was there listening to the two lawyers talk about Jane and frankly, I think I fell asleep for awhile. I kept trying to wave to Jane who was also wearing an orange uniform and even had handcuffs on. She looked like she was crying sometimes, too. I really felt bad. The whole thing was really sad and I didn't want Jane to go to jail at all. And then the judge asked my mom to stand up and asked if my dad's letter was true and she said it absolutely was. The judge didn't smile and looked as mean as before. I didn't like him at all.

So they took a timeout (they called it a recess, but I didn't see anyone go out to the playground) after a lot of talking. That prosecutor guy came over to Jane's lawyer and all of us cause even he had asked the judge to go easy on Jane, but he said it didn't look good at all. Said something about 2 or 3 years in prison. Yikes!!! I guess it's really bad when you run away from the court even if it was when you were a kid. Finally, the judge came back and started to talk and he said a lot of really bad stuff about Jane, that I don't remember except he was very mean to her. And then just like on TV, he asked if anyone wanted say anything before he would tell everyone what was going to happen–that's called the sentence. And I looked around and no one said anything– nothing at all. I mean they had all talked a little before, but no one said a goddam word now–everyone looked plain scared. So I raised my hand like I had always been taught in school and the judge asked if I was the boy in the letter he had read. They told him yes and he asked me to stand up and talk. Well, I stood up and gave him my two cents worth, but unfortunately no one in the whole fucking place could understand a word of what I was saying–which was simply that Jane was my friend and I needed her back at the Market with me. But I got even more tongue-tied than usual, and not even my mother knew what the hell I was saying. The judge looked at me like I was a complete idiot and made a funny face and thanked me for speaking, but just before I sat down, I asked if I could give Jane a hug cause I hadn't given her a hug in weeks and I missed that. The judge still didn't understand what I was saying, but finally my mom said I just wanted to give Jane a hug goodbye. The judge said that was OK, and said I could go over to her. So I walked over and then the policeman next to Jane said, "No touching the prisoner", which was pretty stupid if you ask me, cause the judge said it was OK. And the judge agreed and told the guard to let me give her a hug. And I jumped up and gave her the biggest hug I could and whispered in her ear so no one else could hear, "Jane, guess what? Macho Man Randy Savage and Hulk Hogan won Survivor Series!!" I figured she hadn't heard.

Well, she burst out in tears, then my mom and Diane and Dick started crying for some reason I don't understand, because no one heard what I said except Jane. I mean, I didn't even know they were that interested in who won Survivor Series. Then everyone in the whole fucking courtroom started getting tears in their eyes cause I wouldn't let go of her. I looked at the judge and even his eyes were getting red. He looked embarrassed (yeah, big word but I know it) and slammed his hammer down and called for a recess, though again, no one went out to the playground where there was some fine basketball being played. Everyone stood around and that prosecutor and Jane's lawyer came over and said they had no idea what was going on. Finally the judge came back and his eyes weren't red anymore. And then he started insulting Jane some more and said if he ever saw her again in his court she would have the worst day of her life and that if she ever did anything bad to me, he would personally punish her, and all sorts of nasty stuff. He told her she owed her life to me, which was the dumbest shit I had heard in a long time–after all she was my job coach. I needed her a lot more than she needed me. And then he said she couldn't get a drivers license in New Jersey for the next 10 years, which made no sense at all since she lived in Philly. And then he slammed his hammer and left and that was the end. Everyone sat there and looked like fools cause no one could figure out what had exactly happened. But it turned out, the judge decided not to send her to jail at all and he punished her with no driver's license in New Jersey. Which is hardly a big deal, since I have never had a fucking drivers license in my life! Jane was out in about an hour and we all drove back to Philly and had a nice dinner and I tell you, I got more congratulations from those people for telling Jane who had won Survivor Series than I could have ever imagined. Apparently they all WERE wrestling fans after all.

Chapter 12
Birthday stories

The holidays my family take most seriously are birthdays. Birthdays are important to all of us and we always have a really nice meal. We usually eat out somewhere (always for me), but nowadays my parents are old farts and sometimes my mom just makes a great dinner. And lots of presents, of course. Oh, we do Christmas, Chanukah and Kwanza, since our family believes in any type of celebration, but birthdays are the big thing. In Philly, we went to lots of different restaurants for my birthdays, but three stand out in my memory. The biggest was my 21st birthday, but I'll save that for last.

Frankie's Italian Seafood was one of my all time favorite Italian restaurants and we went there a lot, cause my mom and dad liked it as well–fabulous food. Frankie was the owner (obviously) and he took a real liking to me. At least that's what my parents said cause Frankie wasn't a huggy and happy-go-lucky guy. He always sat at the same small table every time we were there and was always eating large amounts of food. I never saw him not eating. Frankie was so big that when he did walk, he had to use crutches because he was just too big to walk on his own. When he was at that table, he was like a king. Everyone would walk over to him almost scared like, and whisper something into his ear and he would either nod yes or no and keep eating. Didn't talk very much at all. One really weird thing was that people were always walking up and giving Frankie money that he either put in his pocket, or on the table if it was in an envelope and then someone would come by and take it in the back. I even saw policemen come into the restaurant and give Frankie envelopes, so he must have been a real popular guy.

When I came in, Frankie would always wave me over to his table and we always had an arm wrestling match and I always won. He would rub my head and give me a nice little smile and say just a few words, like, "you're a good little man" or "that's my boy". And that was that–we'd go eat.

On one of my birthdays, I chose to go to Frankie's. The rule in our house is that the birthday person gets to pick the restaurant. So my dad called in the reservations and said it was my birthday, and they said fine, Frankie would take care of it. So we got there around 7 o'clock and the place was pretty crowded. And guess what? The whole place was filled with balloons that said "Happy Birthday Shane", at every table, not just ours. And all the waitresses were wearing party hats with the same thing on them. Our table had all sorts of little party gifts for us and for some friends who came with us. It was a really great party and at the end, Frankie made everyone in the whole restaurant sing happy birthday to me. Loudly. And he was watching to make sure everyone sang. It was fantastic. But Frankie never left his table and toward the end of dinner, he motioned for me to come see him. He gave me the only hug he ever gave me and it was really a very warm hug. Then he handed me a $100 bill for my birthday gift. I really didn't know how much that was, but I knew it was big. When I got back to the table and showed it to my parents, my mom said to my dad, "That's very nice, but we can't accept that. It's too much." And my dad agreed. So he called over our waitress who was beautiful and a friend (well, like a restaurant friend) and said, "Would you please thank Frankie for his thoughtfulness and generosity, but it's simply too much for Shane. We really appreciate his kindness." At least that's what my parents say they said when we were writing this book, as well as the following conversations.

The waitress looked like she had been stabbed in the chest and about as scared as anyone I've seen in a long time. She just said, "There is no way I am going over to Frankie and saying that. You can do it yourself, if you want to, but I wouldn't recommend it." My mom, of course insisted and made my dad go over to Frankie, and my dad didn't look too happy either. I guess that's what he told Frankie, who from where I was sitting, barely looked up. Which was strange cause I think he liked my dad and was always nice to him. I am told he replied, "I didn't give it to you. I gave it to the kid. Now give it back to the kid." And apparently, my dad just said thank you and came back to the table.

My mom got a little pissed off when she saw my dad give me back the $100 bill in a way that Frankie could see it and she started to head over toward Frankie, but my dad grabbed her and said, "Drop it. We can discuss this later." And that was that. Except Frankie wouldn't let my dad pay for any of the meal–it was his treat. We all thanked him a lot as we were leaving and without smiling at all, he said, "It was my pleasure."

And you know what? The very next year, my whole special ed class had lunch at Frankie's for my birthday, cause he remembered and invited us all over. Lots of balloons and hats and party favors and once again it was his treat. Frankie was a tough guy but man, he had a great heart.

• • •

One of my other favorite Italian restaurants was a place that's still open to this day, but my dad says he can't use the name, because he doesn't want to get shot. Then he laughed and said it's probably different nowadays, but he still won't use the name and I don't know it–too long a name for me. It was a very nice restaurant and people dressed fancy for that, but my parents always dress like bums and it didn't matter where we went. When I had my birthday dinner there, we went with Mr. Curcio and his whole family and, man, that was a great meal as well. Now I gotta tell you, it's no big secret that in those days, it was sort of a mob hangout. How do I know that? Well, someone came in and tried to shoot someone with a shotgun for some argument over something–it was in all the newspapers. But the food was so good, who cared. And the people who ran it were some of the friendliest people around. My dad says they were not gangsters at all. The owner always personally came over to see us whenever we were there, even though we weren't close friends, just to say hello to me and give me a rub on the head. We got the royal treatment at my birthday dinner. But the really special treatment came from a table right next to us. There were a bunch of old guys with really beautiful young girls by their sides who were barely wearing any clothes. They were really hot. And a few of those big older guys came over to our table to 'pay their respects' as they said and wish me a very happy birthday. They each gave me $20 bills. My mom and dad kept their mouths shut– which shows they are capable of learning. Then one of the guys came over with a box and said to my mom, "You are a beautiful family. Please, pick something from this box as a token of our friendship and affection for your son. He seems to be a very special boy". I mean these guys were just the nicest strangers I had ever met. So then he opened the box and it had a bunch of cool looking jewelry and rings and watches in it. I could tell my mom was getting pretty uncomfortable and in a very meek voice thanked him but said she really couldn't. And the guy smiled and said, "Just pick something out, please. It would be an insult not to take a gift. And we'd like to invite all of you to the back room with us after dinner for drinks and cigars and we can have a nice time for your son." And he pointed to a big brown wooden door in the back.

So my mom took a pinkie ring for me that I have to this day, but it's too big for me so I don't wear it much except every once in awhile on my thumb when we go somewhere special. After he left, my parents talked in whispers coming up with the best excuse why we couldn't go to the back room. I wanted to go but they basically told me to shut up. The Curcios were cracking up and Jeannie, Steve's wife, loved following the mob in the papers and I could tell she really wanted to go. The final lame excuse came from my father, who walked over to their table at the end of dinner and said, "That's so kind of you to invite us to join you for after dinner drinks. But unfortunately, my son has his heart set on previous plans. We have arranged to go bowling with some of his friends and classmates, and really have to get there soon. We don't want to disappoint them." Or at least that's what he tells me he said. Which is one of the most pathetic bullshit lies I have ever heard at 10:30 on a Saturday night. But the guys bought it and smiled and then toasted our table with glasses of something called Sambuca. It was a crazy night, and probably a night that could have had a much better story, if my parents hadn't been such wimps.

• • •

But without a doubt, my greatest birthday party ever was my 21st birthday party at Charlie's old restaurant,

'Something Special'. Charlie closed the whole restaurant down on a Saturday night, which means nobody could eat there the whole night unless they were invited by me. And he and my dad got in a big argument like they always did, cause Charlie wouldn't let my dad pay for anything. They always fought about stuff like that, but I stayed out of it. I was in charge of what is called the guest list. Which apparently, created some problems for some people. You see, it was pretty obvious that all my closest friends and my parents' closest friends would be there, and we had room for like 80 or maybe even a hundred people–I didn't count–but there were a lot of people there. And when it got down to the last 20 or so people to invite, the choices were hard for me. I wanted everyone I ever knew to come cause I'm a very social guy–but there just wasn't enough room for that. Towards the end of the choosing, I decided to invite most of the folks who sat around us at the Temple University basketball games. I live and breathe Temple basketball to this day, even here in Tucson, and I will have a lot to say about that later on. A very special thing. We had season tickets for years and always sat with a group of 'residents' from Temple University Hospital where my dad worked and taught–that means they were young doctors who studied some stuff with him. And since I saw them at the games all the time, they became good friends of mine. I mean, when you scream and yell with friends at basketball games all season long for a few years, you develop something called a 'bond', and we were all definitely 'bonded'. Anyway, when I was done choosing, my dad invited a bunch of them. And that filled Charlie's place up completely. By accident, I forgot to invite this young doctor named Gary and his wife who were really nice friends–just forgot–my bad. Well, my dad came home laughing one day, a couple of weeks before the party, and told my mom that one resident was 'devastated' that he hadn't been invited to the 'social event of the year'. He was the only one left out from the basketball group. The guy actually went to my dad's office to ask about it–according to my dad, he really wanted to go and really liked me a lot. I think my dad was just jerking him around, since there's always room to cram in another two people for anything. But my dad told him that I was in charge of the guest list and said this guy would have to see me for permission to get invited. Gary asked my dad to put in a word for him with me, but my dad kept screwing around with him and said he couldn't do that–the guy just had to ask me personally and I would decide. Which was silly since my dad knew I would have invited any nice stranger off the street to my party if I was allowed to. So about a week before the party, this guy comes to our house to have a sit down and get invited to my party. I remembered him right away, since he was a really good guy and I just forgot to invite him. But I busted his chops a little and said he could come if he got me a good present, which pissed off my parents, since the invites said no presents. Fortunately, no one paid attention to that line and I got tons of presents from everyone anyway.

So we talked for a few minutes and finally I gave him the thumbs up, which made him really happy. I mean he was giddy happy. When the party came, he and his wife were the first to arrive, they stayed the whole time and were the last to leave, and they bought me an official Philadelphia Flyers jersey (actually I got two of them–someone else got me one also), which was a ridiculously expensive gift (my dad yelled at him about that). I still have it and save it for special occasions. I tell you, people can be so damn nice. My best present was from Paul, one of my dad's lifelong friends, whose whole family have been our friends forever and they come to see us all the time. He had a special official Temple basketball jersey made for me with Aaron McKie's number on it, but my name on the back–cause Aaron McKie was my favorite player then–and he became an NBA star. Paul's son, Matt, is my 'brother', that's how close we are. More on that later, too.

Now I'm not going to give you a big long story about the party because there were no gangsters, no crazy stuff like the roof caving in or anything like that. It was just the greatest party because I had every single friend in Philly there and everyone treated me like a king. Oh, there was cool stuff alright. There was a magician from a casino in Atlantic City who was there the whole night doing magic for everyone and he was pretty slick–scared the crap out of my dad's buddy, Bart, with a trick that looked like he was going to chop his hands off. And a belly dancer, who danced with everyone (besides me), like Morris and my dad and Charlie and just about everyone else once they got some booze in 'em. Patrick (one of my dad's best friends) came with his two kids who were real young then and I didn't know them yet, but we got a picture of them watching the party and their mouths were hanging open at the whole scene. I became good friends with them later on.

So no funny stories or strange things that happened. Just the best birthday party ever. A lot of it is 'personal' as my dad says–just the best feelings I ever had being around all my friends on a very important day and I'm not sharing that with you in this book. I learned about crying a little when you are very happy, something I never understood before. I don't think I ever did that again. So that's all we are going to cover about my 21st birthday party. Some things are just private.

Chapter 13
Wrestlers, flips, and a famous politician

I already told you that my buddy, Matt, is like my brother. You know when we first met? The very day he was born, since he is younger than me. I held Matt in my arms straight out of his mother's arms, right in the hospital. Now that's going back a long time. And I've played with Matt ever since–when he was little, when we were about the same size, when he got bigger than me, and even now, when he's a guy with a real important job. Matt has never forgotten my birthday in his life. And he calls me on his cell phone all the time and I call him on mine, whenever I feel like it. And neither of us is ever too busy not to have a real long talk. We talk a lot during basketball season since he is a big Syracuse fan (that's where he went to college) and we argue with each other over who's better all the time–Temple or Syracuse.

Fortunately for me, or maybe BECAUSE of me, Matt became a real professional wrestling fan, especially when he was younger. He doesn't keep up with it as much now, but I fill him in on what's going on nowadays when we talk. But he was a good fan and one time his dad, Paul, and my dad took us to the Spectrum to see WWE wrestling matches, although it may have been called WWF in those days–I can't remember when they changed the name for some reason. I used to go a bit and sometimes with Sammy, who was another of my good Philly friends. He was the grandson of Diane, who I already told you owned the market where I worked. Solid guy.

When Paul and my dad took us, they were sort of assholes to begin with. Matt and I were really excited, but Paul and my dad made fun of wrestling. They said it wasn't a sport, that it was fake. I know some of it is fake, but some of it is real, too, cause it's not fake when you pick up a 300 lb guy over your head and throw him on the mat. These guys are big and strong and beat the crap out of each other and they are funny too. The divas are awfully hot as well. Matt and I didn't like it when our dads made fun of it and we told them to shut up about it when we were walking in the Spectrum that night–and they did. It was the night of a famous "Kiss My Foot Match", which was won by Mabel, but if you are not a wrestling fan, I have learned that will mean nothing to you. And if you are a real wrestling fan, I don't need to explain it. But the funniest thing that night was watching our dads. When the matches started, they hardly watched at all and were talking about other stuff, while Matt and I were screaming our lungs out. That is called rude. But after awhile, when the crowd got real loud, and fireworks were set off, and the wrestlers started talking to the crowd, they started watching more. Then they started laughing at stuff and sort of cheering for some of the wrestlers, though they had no idea who the good or bad guys were, and were cheering for the wrong guys a lot. But by the time the last couple of big matches came, they were completely into it, though I admit I have no idea why they were still laughing so much. They started cheering and then screaming, too. I have no idea why they became so excited, but I think they got caught up in the whole crowd, noise, lights and all that. It made Matt and me have even more fun, cause everyone was high fiving great moves and such. When the Undertaker came out, just before the "Kiss My Foot" match, the place was going nuts and so were all of us, including our dads. When it was all over and we got home, everyone was so hoarse from screaming that we could hardly talk. Our moms asked our dads why they were hoarse and when they explained that they got caught up in the excitement of it all and with me and Matt, our moms cracked up and made fun of them for weeks. They tried to explain themselves, but got nothing but more laughs. And finally, I said in a very small voice, cause my throat really hurt, "If you had come with us, you would understand." And that shut them up real quick, cause I knew that was the last thing they would ever do. But I was wrong, cause one time my mom DID go with me and Sammy and my dad to a WWE event. But she didn't scream or yell–just didn't get it at all. There's just some things you can't teach your mom.

Matt and I did all sorts of stuff together growing up. Played at each other's houses, went to Phillies and Sixers games, played ball together. All the stuff that good friends do. And I knew that I was different from Matt, but he didn't care and neither did I. I couldn't do most things as good as he could, but it made no difference and that is what friends are all about, in my opinion.

There was one thing I think I did better than Matt, and that was doing flips off the top level of my bedroom onto a mattress on the second level down and then doing another flip onto my bed. That's probably because Matt was never a gymnast and I was. When my parents discovered our setup, we were strictly forbidden to ever do it again. They said we would kill ourselves. So we made sure we only did it when we knew they weren't coming near my room. And one of us kept watch while the other did his flips. I mean who the hell are parents to tell you about playing in your room? We weren't bothering anyone and we were very experienced at this. And we almost got away with it for our entire lives together in Philly. But wouldn't you know it–on the very last weekend in Philly, just before we moved to Tucson, Matt and his whole family came over to say goodbye. His little twin sisters went to watch TV and the parents sat around drinking beers and wine. Matt and I went to my room for one last competition. And on one of his very last flips, Matt fell off my bed and broke his wrist. We didn't know if we should even tell our parents, but we did. It really didn't matter, since we were moving and we wouldn't ever be able to play that game again. And like I told you earlier in the book, if you are going to do something bad, make sure you throw in a little injury, so that you don't get yelled at. Which is exactly what happened. Matt got a cast, no one yelled at either of us cause everyone was concerned about Matt, and there was no reason to talk about the mattress flips cause the mattresses were in a moving van in a couple of days. Talk about good luck!

Matt's sisters, Lauren and Amanda are good friends of mine as well, but I didn't hang out with them as much growing up since they are girls and a lot younger than me. But they are very cool. And guess what? I got to hold them on the day they were born, just like Matt. That was a crazy day for another reason. Their dad, Paul, went outside the hospital for some air and came back to get me and my dad, to see some politician. First thing you should know is that this was a very famous hospital–it was the hospital where they took Rocky in the Rocky II movie. I know pretty much everything there is to know about every Rocky movie ever made, as I believe I've already told you. If I haven't, now you know.

So we went downstairs and there's this guy talking to a whole van full of handicappers like me (except they were older, adult handicappers) right in front of the hospital, exactly where Rocky was in the movie. I mean the people were outside the van on the sidewalk, not in the van, maybe about 20 handicappers altogether. He was the politician Paul was talking about. My dad and Paul said they couldn't believe that this guy (who they said was a nobody at the time), was so nice and friendly and was individually talking to each and every one of those handicapped guys and girls to ask them to vote for him. Paul and my dad said it was amazing that he was doing this with no TV cameras around or news reporters and people like that. It was a Sunday and really, there was absolutely no one around. He was just standing there all alone and trying to get those folks to vote for him. With a really big smile and very friendly to everyone. I really liked it when he even came over and shook my hand nice and hard, like a man. And he asked me to vote for him too. He talked to my dad and Paul, and they were very impressed with him for being so good with handicappers, cause there are a lot of people who aren't so good with us. Some people just don't feel comfortable around us, especially strangers, but that's only a small number of people. But this guy was so cool and smooth, that none of us could believe it. You know who he was? President Bill Clinton. Course he wasn't president then, and in fact, Paul and my dad thought he was a little nuts working so hard to get votes from that little group. Hardly anyone had ever heard of him at that time–he wasn't famous at all, and I certainly didn't know who the hell he was until just before he became president and had lots of TV commercials. But everyone at the hospital entrance liked him, so I guess he was really good at getting other people to like him, which is what politics is all about, or so I am told.

That election was the very first time I was old enough to vote. And I got to vote for the guy who personally shook my hand and asked me to vote for him. Not in a big crowd, but directly to my face. That's pretty cool as far as I'm concerned, and it's the only reason I am breaking the secret rule about not telling anyone who you voted for. The other reason I voted for him is that I generally vote for the guy who has the better looking wife and in that election, it was no contest. His wife became famous later on, and now she is running for president. But she got old like me (well, she's actually much older than me), so I don't think her looks matter much anymore.

Chapter 14
Kickball and Graduation

Have I told you about Field Day at Washington School? I believe not. It's a day at the school when they split the whole school into two teams, blue and white teams, and everyone competes in different athletic events like the 50 yard dash, basketball, foul shooting, physical fitness stuff, and lots of other sports. It's a really big deal and everyone takes it very seriously–no screwing around–winning is everything. Bragging rights or something like that. And guess who the boss of Field Day is? You guessed it–my buddy, Dr. Bradley.

My biggest Field Day was several years before I met Bill Clinton, so I am going backwards in time again. I don't see how people can write books with everything in order. I just don't think that's very important.

This particular Field Day changed my life in some ways. Especially at that school. I mean it wasn't like learning how to work a real job, or school stuff, or making a best friend or things like that. It got me something my dad calls 'respect'. I sort of know what that is, but not really. It kinda means people know you are an OK person, but it's more than that. It's sort of like they know they can trust you or something.

Field Day was something pretty much only for the normal kids, except for me and Carmen, cause we were pretty good at sports, like I told you. And Dr. Bradley helped a little too. Even though we were really good at some sports, we really sucked at some others. Or parts of others. Take kickball, which this story is about. I could kick the shit out of a kickball sometimes (and sometimes I whiffed) and everybody knew it, so when it was time for me to take my turn at kicking, kids paid attention. But I never overcame my problem with catching the ball–just about any ball. Just not my thing. So let me tell you the story.

It was the end of the day and I'm talking past the end of the day. It was at least 20 or 30 minutes after the time when school ended, but nobody was leaving because the last event of the day was a big kickball game. And on this particular Field Day, the teams were in a tie, so whoever won the kickball game was going to win the whole Field Day and get ribbons and awards and prizes and all sorts of stuff. That meant that every single kid in the entire school was packed into that playground and watching that game. It was like going to Veterans Stadium to watch the Phillies, there were so many kids there. Carmen and I were on opposite teams to balance things out, since there were a few kids who really didn't want us in that game–it was simply too big a game for us, or so they thought. But no one said much to us cause they were scared Dr. Bradley would find out–not that I would have ratted on them.

My mom always picked me up in front of school in the little red truck and Mr. Curcio went out and told her I would be late because there was a big kickball game going on, I was in it, and it was going to decide who won Field Day. My mom had about as much interest in this as she had shown during my early Special Olympics gymnastics career, so she just sat and waited for me in the truck and never even saw the game itself, but she did get to see what happened when it was over. Scared the shit out of her, too.

Let's just move to the last inning, which was extra innings, because not only was Field Day tied, but the game had been tied for a long time. Finally, my team got a run and all we had to do was hold off the Blue team for 3 outs and we would win the game. Or maybe it was the White team–I can't remember. I went out to the field and took my place in right field almost up against the fence. They put me there for my fielding skills. Which is to say everyone knew that the last person who was going to catch a ball was me. I was cool with that cause I knew I sucked at fielding. Just an 'aside' as my dad puts it–I did kick a single and score a run earlier in the game as reported by Dr. Bradley to my parents–so I did my job already.

Things didn't go very well for us that last inning. We got a couple of outs, but they loaded the bases. That meant one more hit and we would either be tied or we would lose. Lot of pressure on us. Kid came up to the plate, ball got rolled, and 'boom', he nailed it and it looked like a grand slam. Only it was headed right for my part of the right field fence. I watched it coming and soon realized it was going to be right near me–it wasn't going to make it over the fence. Now I wish I could say I made a fabulous jumping catch with my hands over the top of the fence saving the day, but the fence was 8 feet high and I can't jump that high. Lucky for me, it wasn't even going to reach the fence. Unlucky for me, I was going to have to catch the fucking ball or be remembered forever as the 'retard' who lost the whole Field Day for half the school. Those are the facts of life. I wasn't thinking that at the time, but I thought about it later when my parents and I talked about it. What I was thinking about as the ball came down, was to try and catch the goddam ball. Without closing my eyes. I can't describe the catch in any way other than I put both my arms out, kept my eyes open and the ball hit me in the stomach–which was much better than my chest, cause then it would have bounced 20 feet away off me. And I wrapped my arms around the ball. Game over. I was so stunned I caught the ball that I just stood there like an idiot. But my whole team and half the school went nuts cause we won the game and the whole Field Day. Next thing I know, my whole team and it seemed to me the entire White team hoisted me up on their shoulders and paraded me around the schoolyard for several minutes, screaming like nuts. And I was screaming, too. Dr. Bradley came over with the second biggest smile I ever saw him have (I'll tell you in a little bit about the biggest smile he ever had, that I saw) and high fived me and my team. Then they kept carrying me out the schoolyard and into the school, down the main hall, and out the front door. Everyone knew my mom picked me up in her little red truck. So my mom looked out her door and all she could see was this huge mass of screaming kids who suddenly started climbing into the bed of the truck and on top of her roof. They started shaking the truck, banging on all the sides, and just acting crazy. My mom got a little scared and jumped out of the truck and ran over on the sidewalk and looked at the door and saw Dr. Bradley and Mr. Curcio with big smiles. Then she looked back at her truck and saw that all the kids were carrying me on their shoulders, chanting my name, and jumping up and down in the truck, which was bouncing like a kickball. She was clueless and went over to Dr. Bradley and Steve who told her what happened. She started smiling but really had no clue what the hell was going on until that night after my dad and Steve talked about it, and they got all the details. I may have won 5 Special Olympics gold medals in gymnastics years before, but in my long and distinguished athletic career, nothing ever compared to making the winning catch for Field Day with NORMAL kids at Washington School. Sweetest game I ever played in my life. OK, I admit, the catch itself was pretty easy and I think most kids would have made it. But it was a tough one for me and I was just so glad I didn't blow it. Kids looked at me a lot different after that game for the rest of the year. And for a few more years after that, even though I was supposed to graduate that spring, but didn't.

• • •

Graduation rolled around that spring and it was a pretty big event. All the eighth graders were graduating, but only me and Carmen were graduating from the special ed side of things. Probably about 40 or 50 kids were seated on the stage to get their diplomas since the school had a total of 500 kids or so said Mr. Curcio. It was gonna be on to high school for all of us the next year. The auditorium was really hot–no air conditioning in those days–and packed with parents who were all dressed up and had cameras and bunches of flowers and all sorts of cool stuff. It was really exciting. And Dr. Bradley ran a lot of the graduation ceremonies since he was like a head honcho. Judy, our really nice principal also talked a lot too, but I always remember Dr. Bradley as being the main man. Funny how that happens.

One of the funniest things about that graduation was how all the kids dressed. See, my parents were told they needed to buy me a suit and so was Carmen's family. So we each got black suits and white shirts and black ties and black shoes. We looked mighty fine.

But since we were in special ed, none of the normal kids talked to us about how to dress at graduation and I guess Mr. Curcio didn't know about it, cause if he did, he would have been in deep shit with my mom. See, all the normal kids were dressed in white suits with white shoes, black shirts, and white ties. They looked mighty fine as well.

What made it really funny was that Carmen and me were the only white kids graduating that year. Everyone else was black. And my dad's got the blurry pictures to prove that all the black kids were dressed in white and me and Carmen were dressed in black, which is one of the funniest graduation pictures I have ever seen. People were just cracking up for a long time when we all first got on that stage.

There were a lot of happy and funny moments at that graduation and I don't think there have been many like it. I've seen a few and this one was the best I ever saw, but that's probably because it was my graduation. But before I get to that stuff, I have to tell you about something sad, too.

All the kids graduating were sitting on the stage as I said, but there was one chair that was empty and it was covered by a white sheet and had a very pretty flower on it, called a red rose. I asked Carmen what that was about, and he said it was James' chair. And I told him that made no sense since James was dead; everyone knew James had been accidentally killed in something called a drive-by shooting near his house, earlier in the year. Carmen shrugged and just said he didn't know why they had that chair but Dr. Bradley told him it was James' chair.

So before they started the main graduation ceremonies and awards and that stuff, they had a special ceremony "In Memory of James". And Judy talked and Dr. Bradley talked and other people talked about what a great guy James was. And that was true. James wasn't a close friend of mine, but he was always nice to me whenever we were together in gym and stuff. And then they called James' mom up to get his graduation diploma, and she started to make a speech and thank everyone, but she couldn't do it. She started crying. Then lots of people started crying. I looked at my mom and dad in the audience and even THEY were crying. I don't know exactly what everyone had said, but it seems to me that eventually everyone in the whole auditorium was crying, including me and Carmen, and we didn't even know why we were crying. It just happened cause everyone else was crying. It took a good 5 minutes for things to settle down after they helped James' mom sit down and stop crying. I felt really bad that she was so sad and I think it made me think about James a little too. But I still really don't understand dead very well, except in the movies, so it's not something I can explain in this book.

Then it was on to the awards being given out and that's the really fun part, cause you get to clap for friends and all the people you've known at school and it's a real happy time. They gave out a lot of awards, though I really didn't know what most of them were for. Who cared? They were awards!! That's all that counts. Carmen got a really neat looking certificate that he said he was going to hang on his bedroom wall. And he got some good clapping, because everyone loved Carmen. Finally they came to the two biggest awards of the day. Best Student and Best Athlete. And you guessed it, Kareem got the Best Student Award and I was never so happy, cause I have already told you he was my best friend aside from Carmen. He was so damned smart, too. He came up and Judy gave him his trophy, shook his hand, and I think maybe she kissed him on the cheek. Maybe. Though I think he would have been embarrassed, so maybe she didn't–I can't remember everything.

Then Dr. Bradley got up and got ready to give out the Best Athlete Award. There were so many great basketball players at that school that I couldn't imagine who they were going to pick. And we were pretty sure it was going to be the best basketball player because of the guy who was the guest speaker that day. I'll tell you in a minute. Carmen and I bet each other on different guys. I think we bet a quarter, but probably not, since that would have reminded me of the Cupcake Song, a place I never wanted to go ever again.

That's when I saw Dr. Bradley with the biggest smile I ever saw on his face. And for some strange reason, Mr. Curcio was standing next to him. And then they announced the winner and they said MY NAME!!! Dr. Bradley started talking about my physical fitness scores–I always got perfect scores on the Marine physical fitness test cause to me doing a hundred sit-ups or pushups was nothing. I could do chin-ups all day until they told me stop. And he talked about my winning catch on Field Day. But mostly he talked about doing the best you can with your abilities and sportsmanship–no clue–but I think it means not being a whiner and never complaining or getting into fights when you are playing games. And I didn't know what to do so I just sat in my chair until Mr. Curcio came over and brought me over to Dr. Bradley to get a really big trophy, the biggest one of the day along with Kareem's. And you know what? All the kids cheered as loud as they could for me. Everyone did– the normal kids, all the teachers in the school, the special ed kids, all the parents–everyone. And they stood up and clapped too. My mom and dad started crying which was silly, but I grabbed that trophy and shoved it up over my head and got more cheers. It was the best. Mr. Curcio said he already knew I was getting it, but didn't tell my mom or dad.

Then they introduced the guest speaker who got up and he was one of the biggest guys I ever saw. I could tell he was a famous basketball player, but I wasn't sure which one–there are a lot of great basketball players from Philly. He walked over to all the award winners to congratulate them, but gave special handshakes to me and Kareem, cause we won the biggest trophies. And he was there because he was a graduate of George Washington Elementary School himself. That's right–he went to my school, too. That was awhile back though. You know who he was? The "L Train". Lionel Simmons. If you are from Philly, there is no need to say anything more. But if you are not, then I will simply say he was one of the greatest college basketball players in the history of Philly. He was named best player in the whole

US when he went to LaSalle, which is one of my Temple Owls arch rivals, but I love all the Philly teams as long as they are not playing Temple. He was the nicest man and after it was all over, he came up again to congratulate me. What a guy–and he was still playing in the NBA in those days, I think. Now that is a great graduation story, isn't it?

So now it was time to move on to high school. My days at Washington were numbered and it was time to visit some high schools to pick the best one for me. I was a little nervous and I really didn't want to leave Mr. Curcio's class. I had been there a long time. And fortunately, I didn't have to for quite awhile.

Chapter 15
Fighting the system, finally

Towards the end of the year, there was a meeting of me and my parents with a bunch of people like psychologists, Mr. Curcio, and some people called administrators and counselors, to figure out the best place for me to go to high school. One of the most important things to me and my parents was that they had a good computer program, because I was pretty good on the computer and always have been to this very day. It's a great way to learn stuff.

So they sent us to a school pretty close to Washington and we sat in the class for about a half hour to watch my new teacher and see how things ran. The teacher was very young and beautiful, which meant I was pretty much on board right away. But it didn't seem like they were having much fun, and some of the special ed kids were acting up a little crazy–stuff that Mr. Curcio would never allow in his class. But this was high school, I guess. Afterwards, she sat with us to talk about stuff. When my dad asked about the computer program, she said there wasn't one–they had one computer between all the special ed classes and it was broken and hadn't worked since she was there. My mom and dad looked pissed–not at her, but at the situation. They really liked the teacher because she was being truthful with them and told it like it was. She said there wasn't much resources (that means money) for special ed, and they spent most of their time on vocational skills (that means doing work while you are at school). We didn't stay long because it was clear my mom and dad didn't like this school at all. So back we went to another meeting of the same people as before and the women gave us the names of 4 schools all over Philadelphia that did have good computer training in their special ed classes and told us to look at them as better places for me to go. And they said we could pick one of them, if we liked them better. We drove all around the city and I mean really far for 4 days, looking at these 4 schools. Mr. Curcio even went with us to some of them to help my mom and dad figure it out since he was my lifelong computer teacher. They were OK, but nothing compared to Steve. But since I had to move along to high school, we picked this high school way up in the Northeast part of Philly–a long bus ride, but what the hell–at least it seemed like a pretty good school and the teacher was nice enough.

Back we went to another meeting and my parents said they thought this faraway high school would probably be OK and we'd be willing to give it a try. But things were a little different at this meeting, cause there was a new woman at the meeting, who apparently was much more important than everyone else. She was a head honcho administrator. I only know her name as "Skunkhead", which was the name some people at my school and my parents used when they talked about her. Except in public, when they used her real name out of politeness. See, she announced at the meeting that we had no choice of schools, that I was assigned to the original school with the broken computer, and that was that. I don't want to brag or sound like something my dad says is called 'arrogant', but this woman didn't know who she was dealing with. We weren't rolling over on this baby. My dad told her what the teacher at that first school had said about her program and lack of money and how she agreed it wasn't the right place for me. Skunkhead said that teacher was no longer there and things would be improved. My dad asked her how she would know that and she said it was her job, in a real nasty way. My dad replied that kids all over Philadelphia got to go to schools of their choice based on their needs (they call some of them magnet schools) and that was the law. But he was sort of bullshitting as usual cause he was no lawyer and only knew a little of the rules. But he could fake it real good. Skunkhead paid him no mind and simply said the decision was final. She thought she could make up her own rules. Then my dad went over to that first school to see what was what and sure enough, the beautiful young teacher was gone. We never found out if she was fired, quit, transferred, or what, and no one at that school would tell us anything.

The very next day, my dad met with his best buddy, Paul. You know, Matt's dad. Now Paul is a lawyer, but he is something called a business lawyer, and helped out companies more than people. But Paul was one of my best buddies, too, and when he heard what happened, he was almost as pissed off as my parents. My dad asked him to recommend a lawyer for us, cause this time we were going to fight, but Paul was really pissed and said, "I will handle this personally. Nobody is going to fuck over Shano." My dad was sort of shocked and said, "Is this something you can do?" And Paul modestly said, "Yeah, I used to be a litigator (that's like Perry Mason on TV). We are going to kick their asses."

So Paul checked out some stuff over the next few days. Next thing you know, he files something called an "appeal" of the decision and being the smartest lawyer around, he finds some rule that says they can't move me anywhere out of Mr. Curcio's class until the 'appeal' was settled by a State of Pennsylvania Hearing Officer, who turned out to be a judge from the state capitol in Harrisburg. And the reason they couldn't move me wasn't about computers, since he said they could always fake a good computer program that sucked and make me go there. So he said they couldn't move me because it would cause "irreparable social harm for me to be placed in a school that was socially inappropriate for my development level." I have no fucking clue what that meant, which was obviously written by my dad. But it did mean 3 more years in Mr. Curcio's class, because Paul was a master of delaying things and the Philadelphia school district had lots of bigger things to worry about than me and my high school. Since no one was in much of a rush, this was the best thing that ever happened to me in all my schooling. Got to stay with all my friends and lots of teaching to boot for three more years.

I won't go into those extra years with Mr. Curcio, other than to say it was always the best school program for me to be in. Had a great time, and when I did finally leave, it was only for a short time cause I eventually became a high school dropout at age 19.

So after about two and a half years, the court date finally got set and Paul had to get ready to go and convince the judge that I had the right to pick the program most 'appropriate' for my special needs, just like normal kids got to pick some special schools for their needs, even if that meant programs for the really smartest kids of all. No difference according to Paul. Same rules for everyone. I like that.

The hearing was at 6 o'clock in the evening and my dad was frantic with Paul, because Paul never met with my dad about this thing for over two years. He had looked at a few papers in the beginning with my parents, asked some questions and when he got the answers and looked at the papers, he had just smiled and said, "We're fine. Nothing to worry about." But he didn't say anything else and my parents were really worried that Paul wasn't ready. They really freaked when we met Paul at his office at 5 o'clock and he said, "Let's go get a drink first." He was really busting their chops–pretty funny. And he never even asked anything about the case, just chatted real easy like.

When we went into the hearing room in this big building, there were lots of people there. And not just all the people from my school, and the administrators, psychologists, and teachers. There were 'spectators'–people who just wanted to watch. We didn't know who they were, but Mr. Curcio said they were other teachers, parents, teachers union people, you name it. He said a lot of people were interested to see how this went down. He also said he had never seen anything like it before at any appeal.

Remember I said Paul could be like Perry Mason on TV? Most younger people don't know about Perry Mason. It's a TV show–a real old one in black and white. I watched reruns of Perry Mason all the time cause I wasn't even born when it was originally on TV, but Perry Mason was a lawyer who could tear the heart out of a person who was on the big chair and on almost every show, at the end, someone would confess to killing someone else. It was pretty cool. I have no idea why I liked that show, but I also have no idea why I like the show, Mash, and also, All in the Family, since I can't understand much of what they are saying on any episode. I just like certain shows for their feel.

Well, turns out Paul really was Perry Mason. Only better. I gotta let my dad tell most of this story now, cause it's too complex for me, but I definitely added to his writing, since he forgot some of the stuff I remembered. The Philly school lawyer called some witnesses who all said a bunch of shit how all the programs were good for me and that they couldn't just let every special ed kid pick their own school. Blah, blah. And Paul acted as cool as could be and said nothing except to three women, three of the women who were at the meeting to discuss where I would go to high school. He asked each of them only one question and it was a yes or no question, too. Real simple. He just asked, "Did you or anyone at that meeting tell Shane and his parents that they could choose among other high schools, since they didn't approve of his assigned high school?" And all three ladies said, "No." And then Paul said thank you, and sat down with us. I thought my dad was going to pass out, he was so red in the face, but Paul just smiled and told him to calm down, everything was going well. Which seemed like a pile of shit. Cause he let them make speeches about all sorts of rules and regulations and said nothing, except that he reserved the right to call any of them back for questions later. Now I really thought my dad was going to pass out for sure. But that's because he's not a lawyer and he didn't know what Paul was going to do. Paul was going to do a Perry Mason. So when the school board lawyer was finished, the judge turned to Paul and said, "Any witnesses?" And Paul said, "As a matter of fact, I would like to call back exactly three witnesses that have already testified and named those 3 women who were at the original meeting almost 3 years ago to discuss my future high school.

Paul was so slick. He was very friendly to all the ladies, but he kept reminding them in a very polite way that they were under oath and to make sure of their answers, because he said he knew that they would never want to make a mistake and accidentally tell a lie. And then he told them that telling a lie was a lot more serious than where I went to high school to the judge. Which made them all nervous. I could tell. So Paul asked them a bunch of nothing questions to make them real comfortable that nothing was going to happen and made them all very sure of themselves.

And then, on the 1st lady, after a few easy questions, he simply said, "Please remember again that you are under oath. Let me ask you one more time. Did you tell Shane and his family that there were some very good high schools in Philadelphia with special education computer programs for them to look at and that these programs would be much better than the one he was being assigned to? And did you specifically identify 4 schools for the family to visit and evaluate for the purpose of placing Shane there? And that they could pick one of those schools. And did you say this in front of everyone at the meeting, including the following individuals?" And then Paul gave the names of the people at that meeting who none of us remembered except for Mr. Curcio, who wasn't testifying anyway. And two of the names were the other two women Paul had already questioned. And the woman got nervous, but said, "No, I did not."

Paul turned and winked at us and then turned to the judge. He held up a piece of paper and asked that the judge let it be used as evidence just like Perry Mason, and the judge said yes, just like on Perry Mason. He walked over to the woman and asked her what it was and if she recognized it and she said it was a common form about the placement process and yes, she did recognize it since it had my name on it and was dated almost 3 years ago. And it had my mom and dad's signatures on it as well as hers and the other two ladies. And she said it was not an important form, just a routine paper like a whole bunch of others.

Paul turned around with his back to her just like on TV. Didn't even look at her. And said, "Please turn the paper over and read the writing on the other side." The woman turned it over and after a few seconds, looked liked she was going to vomit. She stopped talking but Paul repeated his request. She read off the names of the 4 high schools they had recommended us to visit as better places for me to go. Her voice was trembling and Paul kept winking at us.

"Whose handwriting is that?"

She trembled some more and said, "I don't know."

"We can call a recess and have it analyzed but that seems a waste of time since you know exactly whose handwriting that is. It's yours, is it not? And remember again you are under oath and that perjury is a much bigger crime than anything going on in this hearing."

The woman crumbled. It was fucking Perry Mason time!!! She started sobbing and said yes, it was her handwriting, but that she only said she gave us those names out of our interest to see how these programs worked for future reference and that they were never options for us. Which was a really bad lie and a huge mistake.

"So you gave the family the names of the 4 best special education programs with computers in the city of Philadelphia so the doctor could take off 4 days of work and they could all drive around the city for 4 days to look at these schools that their child was NOT allowed to attend, because it would be of casual interest to them? Do you really want to say that as your testimony? And think anyone is going to believe that? "

And that was that. They had to stop a few minutes so she would stop crying and she finally admitted they had in fact sent us to look at those schools as choices for me to attend. Then Paul brought back the other 2 women, who were so scared shitless at this point that they also cried a little and admitted that was exactly what had happened.

Paul came back to the table smiling a sly little smile and said to my parents. "It's over. We just kicked their asses."

For a minute, it looked like the lawyer for the school board was going to give up, cause he asked for a recess and Paul said they were going to ask to drop the case before the decision and let me go to the damn school. He said that was what a smart lawyer would do. Cause everything everyone from the Philadelphia school district said in that room was now "irrelevant" cause they had all lied under oath. Now is Paul smart or what?

But we watched them on the side arguing, and Skunk-head kept shaking her head no to the lawyer and after about 10 minutes the lawyer came back and said he had nothing else to say, which surprised Paul a lot, but he was pretty relaxed. And then the judge said the hearing was over and a bunch of other shit, and said he would have a final written decision in about a month.

He was an honest judge and a month later, everyone got a copy of his decision. The first thing he said in that decision was that he wanted to apologize for the disgraceful behavior of the Philadelphia School District. He said he had never seen anything like them in his long years as a judge. Or something like that–I couldn't read it myself. Obviously, he had never heard about the shithole town on the Main Line, which was a whole lot worse, but that wasn't very important. No one ever found out what he did to the lying ladies, but no one really cared. Naturally, he said I could now pick any school I wanted to go to in the entire city of Philadelphia, and not just the 4 schools we looked at. But the best part was how he punished them and treated me like a king.

He ORDERED the school district to provide me with free transportation to and from whatever school I picked, and then ordered that the transportation would be in my own private taxi cab. Yup, I went to high school that next year every day in my own private taxi cab!!

And not just any taxi cab, since the driver had to get to know me and be aware of exactly when to come and pick me up, where to drive me and drop me off, know who was going to meet me and that sort of stuff. That's when I met Abdul, who became my private driver. Except a couple of weeks when he was on vacation and his brother was my driver. Abdul and I became great friends that year and we made lots of side stops, both to and from school. We always went to a Wawa (that's like a 7–11 store) and got milk, donuts, cokes or hot dogs for me, and he got other stuff. And sometimes we'd park at a nearby little park and watch birds and squirrels while we ate. And then we'd go home. We had a great time. He played this really weird music from the country he was from and it was good stuff–you could definitely dance to it and we would play it as loud as our ears could take it and rock that cab all over the place. That new high school didn't turn out to be very good for me (though they were all good people), but my taxi rides were worth the effort.

I don't want to bad mouth the high school cause everyone was nice and the teacher was trying her best, but she really wasn't very good on computers–I think I knew more than her. And the whole thing was really about working at school, not learning at school. They taught us about cleaning bathrooms, mopping floors, cleaning rooms, throwing out trash and that sort of stuff. Well, they tried to teach me that, but I told them to fuck off, in those exact words. I didn't have to do that stuff at home, and the normal kids didn't have to do that at school, so why the hell should I? My parents were pretty calm about it, but got called in to see her real quick when I was being a hard ass about it. And they agreed with me.

At the meeting, the teacher explained that the State of Pennsylvania required teaching everyone to clean shit up, cause it prepared them for jobs–it's called "vocational training". She said she was required to do that and we all thought she was telling the truth. We called it bullshit, at least for me. I already had 2 or maybe even 3 jobs by then. And then something happened that I never understood, but I'll let my dad tell it now. One of my classmates came by while we were talking and asked for a magazine and it was some sort of girly magazine and then he went into the bathroom. My parents looked shocked and the teacher said that they allowed the boys to go into the bathroom for 'private time'. I thought my mom was going to fall out of her chair. My dad looked really strange, too. And he said, "So all the boys spend time cleaning toilets and having 'private time' in the bathrooms? Do they wash their hands afterwards?" He later said he was being something called 'sarcastic'. And the teacher said, "I guess they do, but I can't check because it's the boys bathroom and they need their privacy."

Well, my mom and dad then told her they didn't want any vocational training for me, nor any private time, though I never really heard that word until we were writing this book and I still don't know what they were talking about, though I do like reading magazines with pretty girls (like the Divas in the WWE), sometimes in my room. But that's not something I ever did in any school.

I think the word was already out not to fuck with my parents, so I never had to clean bathrooms and mop floors (except at the Market and rarely at Charlie's when we weren't screwing around) and I got to work on the computer or watch a movie, while the other kids worked. And here's one other funny thing that happened after that meeting with my parents. See, that class had a bake sale every week to raise money for something in the school, but I don't know what. My parents always made sure I had money and bought some stuff, because they wanted to support the school. But after they talked about 'private time' and cleaning bathrooms and stuff, my parents told me to just give them the money, but to give away anything I got, to anyone I wanted to—and I made some friends that way. People like gifts, but my mom and dad never ate one of those cookies or cupcakes ever. Weird.

I went to that school for a year, but the best thing about it was really riding back and forth with Abdul. And getting sent to the principal's office. I went there once, and I'm telling you, the women in there were the hottest babes I ever saw. And they really liked me. So I would do anything I could to get sent to the principal's office–run errands, run messages, or even get in a little trouble if necessary, just so I could hang out with them. They would all give me hugs and little kisses and just loved me. I have Polaroids to prove it, man.

But as it turned out, we just bagged the whole school thing after that year. I became a high school dropout at age 19, though I was supposed to go until I was 21. We all agreed it was just not right for me. So it turned out that the best thing about the whole court case wasn't getting to go to the school I picked out, it was getting to stay in Mr. Curcio's class for 3 extra years, which was about the greatest thing that could have happened to me. Funny how things work out.

Chapter 16
The Italian Market on 9th

I already told you about the 9th Street Italian Market, but if you've never been there, you can't really understand it. It's the greatest place in the world to shop for food and eat food while you are shopping. Almost every Saturday, my dad and I and Steve went there to get a whole bunch of stuff. And lots of times, Steve's kids, Paul and Julia came with us–I could always make them laugh cause they were younger than me. Did I tell you how smart they are, especially grown up? Julia writes plays and stories and they are very good–my mom and dad like them a lot, but they are hard for me to understand. Cause she's just too smart. Paul is so smart, he was on the TV show, Jeopardy, which is the hardest game show on TV. He won a ton of money and was on the show as the winner for several days. I have never been able to answer a single question on Jeopardy in my entire life. But I'm pretty good at Wheel of Fortune and Family Feud. And I think I could kick Paul's ass in Deal or No Deal, cause I just know which case the money is in all the time.

Anyway, 9th Street is not like a supermarket. You go to

a different store for almost each thing, not just one big store. That's because each individual store makes their thing better than anyone else. You want cheese, you go to Claudio's, sausages are at Sonny D'Angelo's, stuffed peppers at Di-Bruno's, pork is at Cannuli's, produce is at a lot of different places–you gotta check each thing out individually–but we went a lot to Joey Giordano's. And all along the way you stop to eat different stuff–like some coffee and cannolis at a couple of great bakeries, or roast pork sandwiches, or even better, we'd get takeout at the end of the day from some Italian places off 9th Street and go back to Steve's house, where his wife Jeannie would heat it up and put out some of her own homemade tasties. Like meat and cheese pastries from the ladies at Cacia's Bakery who everyone loved cause they were the craziest, meanest ladies you ever met. They yelled at you if you were a paying customer. Or St. Joseph's cakes from Pepito's. My favorite was always tomato pie from Iannelli's–if you haven't had it, then you haven't tasted a real delicacy. But everyone had their own favorites and there is no better way to spend an afternoon than a nice sunny day on 9th Street. And you always bumped into friends everywhere you went. We even ran into Coach Chaney a few times (I'll be getting to him next chapter), cause he is a real gourmet.

My favorite food is and has always been pasta. And the best place to get pasta was the Superior Ravioli Company. It got sold just before we moved and I'm not knocking the new owners personally, other than to say we went one time after it was sold and we never went back. A group decision, not mine. Just an opinion passed along.

The Superior Ravioli Company was an old place that sold all sorts of great pasta, not just ravioli. I don't even know who owned it, but I sure as hell knew who worked behind the counter and sold us our pasta, which was usually fresh made fettuccine–regular fettuccine, spinach fettuccine, hot pepper fettuccine, garlic and herb fettuccine–just about any fettuccine you could think up. Her name was Antoinette and she was like a grandmother to me. I didn't exactly feel like she was my grandmother, but she would go nuts when we came in and I was there. She'd run around the counter and give me a hug and a kiss and just be all over me. No clue, but it was fine with me. Could have been better if she was about 30 years younger, but I was OK with it. Anyway, the way it worked was she put the bag on a scale and if you asked for a pound of fresh fettuccine, she grabbed it by the handful and filled your bag until it read a pound. Then because she was such a good person, she would throw in an extra handful to make sure you got more than a pound. Pretty nice, don't you think.

Well, when I was there, she would just be so excited and happy to see me and talking to my dad about me and asking all sorts of questions about what I was doing and being so friendly, that she would fill the bag to a pound and then keep adding handfuls of pasta while she kept talking, without looking at the scale. My dad thinks she knew exactly what she was doing, but the bottom line is that when she was looking at me, we got two pounds of fettuccine for the price of one. And so would Steve, cause he was with me. After the first few times this happened (and it happened for years afterward until the place sold), Steve happened to drop by to get some pasta during the week without me around. Yeah, you guessed it, he got a little over one pound of fettuccine for one pound of fettuccine. No special deal. As I told you, Mr. Curcio is a real smart guy so he came up with a brilliant plan. We went to one of those photo button stores, where they make a huge button you can pin on your shirt with any picture you want on it. So we had them take my picture and Steve now had a 4" button of me, to put on his chest. Back he went during the week to see Antoinette and order some bags of fettuccine. Well, when she saw my picture, she went nuts and started asking Steve how I was doing and where was I, and he would say I was fine and asked about her and tell her I couldn't wait to see her again next Saturday. She got very excited just seeing the goddam button with my face on it. And Steve bought 3 one-pound bags of fettuccine. Which weighed about 6 pounds. Mr. Curcio is a genius.

In all the years we went to the Italian Market, we had only one bad experience. That was a rainy day and we were driving over to Steve's house to pick him and his kids up to go shopping and eating. All of a sudden, some guy without a shirt on and no shoes (it was really cold, man) ran right in front of our car while it's going down the street, jumped up on our car hood, slid across it and landed flat on his back on the street. We pulled over and my dad yelled to me to stay in the car, but I rolled the window down to listen. The guy was mumbling, but was totally out of it, and a pool of blood was growing under his head. My dad remained cool but I could see he was very concerned. He put his hand under the guy's head, and he later told me he was scared he was going to feel the guy's brain, but it turned out to be just a bad cut on his scalp. My dad held it with his hand to stop the bleeding just like he did if any of us got a cut at home. And then he yelled at the people gathering around to call an ambulance. A few minutes later, two ambulances arrived and one came to us and the other went a block down a side street. Then the police came and a really nice policewoman whose last name started with Z came over to us to help. She was on the radio for a while and by that time my dad had figured out that the guy was just drunk. The ambulance called in to some little hospital nearby, but my dad acted real important (which he NEVER does) and yelled at them to take him to the Trauma One hospital closest by, which was called Jefferson. He later said he didn't want the guy killed at the crappy hospital and then get blamed for it. So they took him away to Jefferson and my dad told the nice policewoman what happened. Then he asked what was up with the other ambulance down the street. She laughed and said that the guy who ran into our car was drunk in his living room and looked out the window and saw someone stealing his car. So he ran out his door in the rain with just his pants on, to chase his own car down the street. Turned out that the guy who stole his car was also drunk and only made it about one block when he ran into a parked car and passed out at the wheel. They said he seemed like he was going to be OK, too.

By that time, I weaseled my way out of the car and was hanging out with the policewoman, who let me look at her gun (in the holster unfortunately) and then let me sit in her police car, which was the coolest car I ever sat in. All sorts of lights and buttons and stuff. She was real nice to me.

So my dad said to the policewoman, "Is it me, or is everyone in this neighborhood drunk."

She laughed real loud. "No, everyone in this neighborhood is a fucking idiot."

My dad shook his head. "Somehow, I think I'm going to be hearing from a lawyer about this."

"No, doc, you won't. I'm gonna talk to him at the hospital and tell him how you stopped his bleeding and sent him to Jeff and took really good care of him. And it certainly wasn't your fault, it was his."

We went ahead shopping that day, but I could tell my dad's mind was somewhere else. Everyone had to repeat what they said to him three times instead of the usual two times to get his attention.

A few weeks later, my dad got a packet in the mail and started cursing. It was the lawsuit, at least that's what my mom told me. I knew about courts now. My dad mumbled the whole night. "Motherfucking piece of shit."

A couple of weeks later we went to a Phillies game. We

parked across the street from Veterans Stadium and were in a big crowd of people at the crosswalk, waiting for the light to change and the cops to direct us across the street. Big crowd. As we were walking, I saw the nice policewoman was one of the police directing traffic and people walking, so I ran over to say hello. I recognized her right away. My dad followed me and he recognized her too and she remembered us. She was all smiles and asked how we were doing. And then my dad said, "I told you that guy would sue me."

"No way, doc. That little fucker is suing you? I talked to him at the hospital and I told him everything in a real nice way how you helped him out and not to do that. That little prick."

She was good at cussing, that policewoman.

"Guess your talk didn't work."

"Don't worry doc, we're gonna have another talk real soon with a couple of my partners to explain the situation to him. You ain't getting sued."

"Thanks much, but there's really not much to do at this point."

"Just don't worry about a thing doc. It's all taken care of. Enjoy the game." And she slapped me five goodbye.

And my dad never got another letter from a court, a lawyer, or even the police about that accident. Never heard a word about it ever again.

Chapter 17
Temple University – My College

Temple University is the greatest place in the world to me. I told you my dad worked at the hospital there for part of the time we lived in Philly, and he liked it a lot and made some of the best friends of his whole life there. But that's not why Temple is the greatest to me. For me, it's all about Temple basketball.

We started going to some games even before my dad was working there and loved it. Became season ticket holders pretty quick. See, in those days they played in a place called McGonigle Hall, which was about the size of my high school gym. My dad says it held about 3,000 people. I don't know numbers that big, but it was a helluva lot smaller than the Spectrum or Williams Arena that I went to in Minnesota to see the Golden Gophers. Lots of people made fun of it being so small, but we loved it, cause it was so loud–you couldn't help but get excited when 3000 people were screaming their heads off in this tiny little gym. And the teams were great, too. But for me, Temple basketball was all about Coach John Chaney.

If you know anything about basketball, you know about

John Chaney, cause he is very famous. He is in the Basketball Hall of Fame–that's how famous he is. But I know a lot more about Coach Chaney than a lot of people, because he became my good friend. In fact, when he got into the Hall of Fame, he sent me his Hall of Fame T-shirt (personally signed to me), after we had already moved to Tucson. But I got a lot to tell you in between.

I would see him on TV in Philly a lot when I was watching sport news and stuff and I just liked him right away, even before I ever met him. And at every game we went to, I would bug my dad to go down and talk to him after the game. But my dad, being a putz, would never let me go down to meet him. Said Coach was too busy. So after a year or two, I just got fed up with my dad. At the end of one game, he turned around to talk to some of the folks we sat with and I saw my opening. I was off like a shot right after the final buzzer (we won, naturally) and I made it to the floor where Coach Chaney was standing, talking to a couple of people. I just ran right up to him, pulled on his sweater and put my hand out to him and said, "Great game, Coach." Pretty lame, but that was all I could think of at the time and about one of the few things I could say that anyone would understand easily.

Coach turned around and looked down at me and gave me a gigantic smile and said, "Thanks, little man." And then we both started talking basketball, but neither of us had any idea what the hell the other one was saying. I was talking defense, how the guys had to keep their hands up more. I am still fixated on that to this day, when I now discuss this with Coach Dunphy occasionally. But Coach Chaney thought I was talking about shooting and was talking offense and stuff. Didn't matter. We became friends in that moment. By the time my dad found me on the floor with Coach, we were in a heavy basketball discussion that admittedly was 'incoherent', but we were both smiling like idiots. My dad came up and started to apologize for me bothering Coach, and then Coach did the craziest thing. He yelled at my dad. "What are you apologizing for? This here's my friend and you don't ever apologize for him talking to me. What's his name?"

My dad was completely baffled. "Shane. Lot of people call him Shano." He didn't know what else to say.

And then Coach looked at me and said, "You be sure and come see me after the next game, you hear me?" And he looked at my dad who nodded back to him. "I gotta go now, but I'll see you next game."

Next week, sure enough, we went down to see him after another win—my dad never took me down after a loss, but that didn't happen often. And guess what? Coach gave me a big smile and grabbed my hand and walked over to one of his assistants and a minute later, I had a brand new Temple basketball practice jersey.

I can't say I saw him after every game, but I saw him after a lot of games for many years. And sometimes I'd walk with him toward the locker room and even got to look inside a few times. It was so cool meeting players and other coaches. And here's something I bet a lot of people don't know about Coach Chaney. When we went toward the locker room, you went down the hallway and that hallway was always filled up with little kids like me, except they were 'normal' and younger and from the neighborhood around Temple. And Coach Chaney seemed to know them all by name too. And always stopped to talk with them, even for just a little bit. And I saw him give them presents too. He always treated kids extra special whenever I saw him.

OK, I'm not going to talk about all the famous things that Coach did, cause there's books and newspaper and Sport Illustrated stories all about him. And he would be on TV during Christmas and tell funny stories and give away fancy ties. But there was one really cool time, when

Temple won a big game and by the time I got to the floor to see him, guys were setting up lights and cameras for an ESPN interview. I watch SportsCenter several times a day, so I know about that stuff. So I got a hold of Coach and we started talking about the game and laughing and then one of the ESPN guys came up and told Coach they were ready. And you can imagine what Coach did. He started yelling at the ESPN guy. "Do you see I'm having a talk with my friend here? Don't interrupt us. I'll be there when we're finished." The guy walked away very confused. So we talked another minute or so and then slapped five and he was off to his interview. My dad said it was the craziest thing–but I knew that Coach knew how to be polite to his friends.

Those games are some of my greatest memories, and I already told you about all the friends I made in the stands over the years. And I met some cool players, too. But there was a lot more to come, which really made me the greatest Temple Owl fan in the USA.

I gotta jump ahead now, so I can stick with the Temple story and after that, I'll come back to the start of the Tucson years in more detail. Yeah, it's confusing and my dad says this isn't the right way to tell the story, but I told him tough shit, this is the way we're telling it.

After we moved to Tucson, I didn't hear a lot from Coach for a few years. Just lost touch. Nobody's fault, just didn't connect. I blame my dad. I always blame my dad. But my mom saved the day. Finally, Temple was coming to play a game in Phoenix, which is only a couple of hours from Tucson and we got ready to go up and see the game and Coach. But they were playing Arizona State University in a really big arena that the Phoenix Suns play in, and my dad said he wasn't sure we would get to see Coach, cause of the big crowd. But my mom is smarter than my dad, and she got on the phone. She called Al Shrier, who my dad knew just a little. Al Shrier is so important at Temple University

Department of Athletics, that they hung a banner from the rafters with a picture of his briefcase on it–a banner just like the ones with all the famous players and coaches. You gotta admit, that's a pretty funny and very cool banner to put up. What a great guy, though I never met him myself – but I always saw him at the games with his famous briefcase. And what he did for my mom was really special, cause he gave us the private cell phone number of Larry Dougherty, who is basically my all-time best friend ever at Temple. He's a very important guy at Temple with a big long title and he's in charge of a lot of important stuff in Temple's athletic department. He's in a Hall of Fame, too–it's called the CoSIDA Hall of Fame–that's College Sports Information Directors of America–yeah my dad had to write that out. So Larry's pretty famous and important, too. Know how I know that? He got a big award once, and I watched the ceremony on my computer and he gave a big speech. And in the middle of the speech he told everyone why they did their jobs and why they love their jobs. And then he said my name to everyone there and said I was a good example of why they did their jobs. And gave everyone the link to my YouTube video so they could see me. Imagine that.

So my mom called Larry, who was and is the nicest guy in the world, even though he didn't know any of us from a hole in the wall. My mom explained that I was an old friend of Coach and that I really wanted to see him. And Larry set everything up, cause Larry is one of the best guys in the world. We went to the Phoenix hotel the team was at, and Larry met us and we all hung out in the lobby waiting for the team and coaches to come down, cause they were having some sort of meeting. When Coach got down, he saw me right away and gave me a big hug. And even though he yelled at my dad that other time, he gave him a hug and my mom, too. Then my mom and him made fun of each other for some things–just joking around. Coach introduced me to his good friend, Coach Ellerbee, who was a great guy, too. And then other coaches, and players and just about everyone there. And then they passed around a cool white Temple basketball cap and everyone signed it for me. There are NBA players on that cap and it's sitting in my room right now between all my other Temple stuff. And this was like an hour or so before the game–I mean the guys were already dressed in their uniforms and sweats, cause the bus ride to the arena was only like 5 minutes. We had to say goodbye then, since there wasn't going to be time to hang out after the game. But Coach said he would keep in touch. And he did, mostly because Larry said he would make sure of it. See, Larry runs a lot of stuff like I told you, and he always remembered to make sure that Coach and the players did keep in touch with me. From then on, I felt like a member of the gang with all the coaches and players. Coach Chaney always called me on my birthday every year. After big games on TV, Larry would call us and he'd put my favorite players on the phone to talk to me. After I talked to Coach, of course. Like Mardy Collins, Dionte Christmas, Pepe Sanchez, Lavoy Allen, Ramon Moore, Rahlir Hollis-Jefferson, Khalif Wyatt, Will Cummings, and nowadays, "Q"–his name is Quenton DeCosey, but all his friends call him Q. He is my favorite player right now, and he has talked on the phone to me a bunch of times. All these guys play pro basketball now in either the NBA or in Europe or will be soon. But they always had time to talk to me and so did some of their other teammates. Larry just put 'em on the phone for me. Boy, is that cool. And you know what? After a while, I realized that I liked talking to Larry just as much as any player or Coach, because I finally understood that he was a great friend. One of my all time best friends.

In 2006, Coach Chaney retired. That means he was tired and needed to relax. My dad did the same thing a few years ago, which is really a good thing, cause we get to hang out together a lot. With my dad, that is–not Coach. But Coach still called me on my birthday for several years after he retired, since that is what good friends do. When he retired, I figured things might change at Temple, but I always knew I would never stop rooting for them. I never guessed what would happen next.

About a month after Coach Chaney retired, they had a big thing on ESPN called a 'press conference' announcing the new coach who was going to take Coach Chaney's place. I was a little sad at the time but I watched the show anyway. And this pretty nice guy came up and got introduced and his name was Coach Fran Dunphy. Small world–he was the basketball coach at the University of Pennsylvania where my mom and I went to school, but she never took me to any of those games. She just doesn't know basketball very well. So I never met him in my life. We all watched, and about 30 minutes after the show was over, the phone rang and it was Larry. He told my dad to put the speakerphone on, and the next thing you know, I'm talking with Coach Dunphy!! He said he was really looking forward to meeting me one day and that he spoke with Coach Chaney and knew how much support I gave to Temple basketball and that he hoped I would continue to be a great supporter and fan, even though Coach Chaney retired. I'm talking a half hour after he was on the TV!!! Of course I told him, "You bet, Coach!" And then we had a short conversation about basketball strategy just like I used to have with Coach Chaney–you know–the one where neither of us really has any idea what the other guy is saying, but at the end we totally agree on everything. It didn't take me any longer than that phone call to become one of the biggest Coach Dunphy fans ever. I was so happy he called me, cause I was a little worried about the team after Coach Chaney retired. And naturally from then on, he always called me on my birthdays, too. And after some of the big games on TV. I think Larry reminds him, cause he is a very busy man.

In 2011, I went to heaven. No, I didn't die, it's a figure of speech according to my dad. My Temple Owls made the NCAA tournament and were playing the first and second round games in TUCSON about a mile from my house at the McKale Center!!! I don't know if I have the days right or not but I think they played on Friday and Sunday. Or maybe Thursday and Saturday. Whatever. They flew into Tucson a couple of days before the first game in the evening and the first thing that happened was Larry and my dad went to eat and drink beers, while the team practiced the second they got off the plane and into town. Typical for my dad and maybe for Larry, too.

Next day was the greatest–I mean the greatest. The practice was closed to the public–I mean really closed, cause they had a couple of cops at the doors of the high school gym to keep people out. But it wasn't closed to me or my mom and dad. When the bus pulled up and they got into the gym, Coach Dunphy came right over to me and gave me a really big hug like he had missed me for years, even though we had never met face-to-face before. I know he was really busy, but he made sure to see me first. Naturally Larry gave us all big hugs, too. And lots of players and people slapped me five, but they were busy worrying about the game against Penn State coming up. So was I.

That practice was a blast. Right off the bat, Coach Duke (he's a very important coach, too) got 'em started and then Coach Dunphy started his coaching. Pretty quick, he was using some mighty fine cuss words and the players were real serious. All of a sudden, Coach looked over at my mom, since we were standing right by the court, and my dad says he probably wasn't used to closed practices with unexpected visitors. I think he was sort of a little like me–worried that my mom was going to yell at him for cussing. But she just smiled at him, cause my mom can cuss, too, and he gave a tiny smile, and went right back to his coaching like we weren't even there. It was great watching how they did everything. I had never seen that before. I started wandering around and took some shots at side baskets out of the way and hanging with some people I didn't know, but who quickly became friends. Like the Temple radio announcers, Harry Donahue and John Baum. John was one of the greatest players in Temple history and I've emailed him a few times, too. There were the Temple video guys who took movies of lots of stuff and were really funny and nice to me. And then after awhile they said they wanted to interview me!! Just like on TV. Naturally, who is going to turn down an offer to be interviewed about Temple basketball. So they filmed an interview with me and my dad about basketball and Temple and later they interviewed Coach Dunphy about me, and they took all sorts of pictures of the practice and everyone was laughing and kidding around. It was really fun playing pretend. So we had dinner with Larry and his cool assistant Alex–I think my dad and Larry had a lot of meals and beers that week and my mom and I got to go to some, too.

But then it was game time against Penn State, and without exaggerating, it was the most exciting game I think I ever saw because Juan Fernandez hit the winning shot with less than one second left in the game. We were all screaming so loud at that game that we were all hoarse–even worse than the night at WWE. Next day, we skipped morning practice, but then Larry called and said to get our asses up to the resort where they were staying cause they were taking the team pictures and we sure didn't want to miss that. So my dad and I went up to meet Larry and the team arrived back from practice in their nice white sweats, to take team pictures. I was at the bus door and slapped five with every player as they got off, and they were the best. It was sorta hot (Tucson is in a desert, in case you didn't know) and they wanted to move fast so the guys didn't get tired–they weren't used to the heat like us Arizonans–or so my dad says. So they posed the team in front of the Catalina Mountains that we visit sometimes, and took pictures of just the players quickly, then they yelled out "coaches", and all the coaches got in the picture and they took some more of those. Then they yelled out, "all staff", and then all the team managers and trainers got into the group and they took a bunch of those pictures. All of a sudden, they yelled out, "Shano". Damn, they were going to take a picture of everyone with me in it! I wasn't really ready, but I did my best. Fortunately, I had on my Aaron McKie #23 Temple cherry basketball jersey on and I pulled down my Temple hat on my head, kept my shades on and walked right in front of the whole team and stood about 20 feet in front of them, with my arms crossed and my best 'homeboy' look. Well, that brought the whole house down–I really got them laughing. Cause I looked like the team owner according to Larry, standing so far out in front of everyone. They told me to step back and I thought they meant one step and I did that. More laughing. Finally, one of the guys came from behind and dragged me back to the first row of players (right in the middle), but I kept my homeboy look the whole time. They took a bunch of pictures and so did my dad. And they sent me my official team picture to my email later that day. And it looked great. But my dad's pictures were funnier, cause he caught Lavoy, Scootie, and Khalif in THEIR homeboy poses just like me, with their arms crossed and tough-ass look, but laughing, too. What a great time we had that afternoon.

When we got home, the phone started ringing. A lot. All of a sudden, a bunch of friends from Philly started calling. Some of them we hadn't heard from in a long time, but they were very excited. We were on TV in Philly. There's a lot of people in Philly who watch TV and it turned out that the 'pretend' video from practice became a real video and one of the TV stations put that video on the news broadcast. It was a video that said I was probably the best Temple fan of all and it opened with me hitting a shot just inside the 3 point line (good thing I didn't know they were filming–would have made me nervous), and me getting interviewed. And my mom and dad and me talking with Coach, and they even had Coach talking about me–right in the middle of the tournament. I was a celebrity. I'm not kidding, even some strangers who we didn't know called our house saying I was the most beautiful person they had ever seen–my dad said they were a little crazy–but I didn't care, I was a star. And it's on YouTube with lots of hits (not like Michael Jackson or anything, but very respectable). If you want to see it, here's the link: https://www.youtube.com/watch?v=3P19gzkPKcQ

The next game was against San Diego State and they were real good. They had Kawhi Leonard, so that tells you something. It would have been the single greatest game I ever saw because it went double overtime, but unfortunately we lost. So it was great, but only up until the end. Cause if you lose, it just isn't a great game anymore. I mean it's a good game while you're watching but it's a sad game when it's over. We waited outside the locker room door with the Athletic Director, Bill Bradshaw (a really nice guy who gave me a special Temple pin), to say goodbye to everyone and I was nervous that everyone would be too sad. And when each player came out, they really did look bummed out and looking down. But when they saw me and I gave them the thumbs up and told them they were great, they all smiled and gave me hugs goodbye and even took pictures with me, to remember everyone. Larry said that me being there helped them smile a bit and that made me feel good. That was one of the best weeks of my life.

Now, sometimes Larry gets me surprise birthday presents. Like a few years ago, my parents secretly told everyone

I knew and they knew, to send me a Happy Birthday email, since I love getting email. Well, Larry had a whole bunch of his friends in the sports world from around the country send me emails, including some of the former players who were playing pro ball in Europe. I got a total of 584 birthday emails in one day between my friends, Larry's, and my parents'. And I made my dad type out my reply email to every single person, which took a few days, but he would have done that anyway. A couple of years ago, there was a game on my birthday and it was on CBS nationally. Larry talked to Alaa Abdelnaby and Tom McCarthy, who were announcing, and right in the middle of the game they gave me a birthday shout-out for everyone in the whole country to hear–what great guys! And last year, Larry did a birthday video from Temple itself with all the Temple cheerleaders (I love cheerleaders) screaming out happy birthday, and then a whole bunch of players saying happy birthday to me, then my radio friends Harry Donahue and Big John Baum, and then Coach Aaron McKie saying happy birthday–and he's probably my all-time favorite player from Temple. Then Coach Dunphy was at his desk and said a beautiful happy birthday message and called me his brother (I loved that). Finally, Larry gave me the biggest happy birthday wishes of all and my dad said I didn't stop smiling for a week.

Well, I still am the greatest Temple fan of all, no matter what anyone else claims. We talk to Larry all the time, Coach Dunphy never forgets my birthday and still calls after big games too, and when Larry calls right after games, he always puts some of the guys on the phone to say hello. Especially Q. I'm part of the team, man.

The Tucson Years

Chapter 1
New Town, New Friends

As you can imagine, I could tell you more Philly stories. I could do two or three more books just about my life in Philly, because those were what are called my 'formative' years. But my dad said enough is enough, and he told me to stop bugging him about more Philly stories, because readers probably had enough already. So it's on to Tucson, but it's too bad I couldn't tell you about some pretty funny stories involving the police and me. Some other time.

So we moved to Tucson about 20 years ago. Seems like just yesterday. I have no idea why we moved here, except we once had a vacation here and all liked it and it had something to do with my dad's job. We first moved to a place called the Foothills, just outside Tucson, which was all these really nice houses with lots of desert land around them and wasn't like any place I had lived before. My dad rented a house there, so he wouldn't make the mistake he made in Philly when he bought that beautiful house in that shithole town on the Main Line. It was a great house, with a great view of beautiful mountains behind us and you could see the whole valley of Tucson, with the downtown part of

Tucson way far away. And the downtown is my favorite part of Tucson. And you could see the University of Arizona far away, too, and I like going there for stuff. But the house where we lived was pretty weird, cause there was nothing much around except other houses. You had to drive if you wanted to get anywhere, which was a lot different than most places I lived.

So the first day we got there, I headed down our very long driveway. My dad says it was about 50 yards long–all I knew was that I was tired by the time I got to the end of it cause we were already working on the house, and the sun was very bright even though it wasn't that hot, being February. I sat down right alongside the street it went into. I think I saw 3 cars pass by, over about an hour. Then my mom came down the driveway looking for me. I didn't get in trouble cause I told them I was going for a walk and they knew I would listen to them and not leave our property. They trusted me.

When my mom got to me, she sat down with me and we looked at the mountains and the view and relaxed a few minutes. Then she asked what I was doing down there and I explained to her I was waiting for a taxi to flag down, to get a ride all the way downtown to check it out. She cracked up and said it didn't work that way in Tucson–you couldn't just wait for a cab to come. She said a cab would never come. I told her that made no sense and asked if we were in a different country. She laughed and said, "Sort of." And she was right, too. Never saw a damn taxi ever pass that house the whole two years we lived there.

But I really did like that house a lot. My first home swimming pool, ever. Hot tub, too, though we never had one of them again when we moved downtown. I mean, why would anyone ever NOT have their own swimming pool and hot tub. I was in that pool for 8 months of the year and I've had a pool at my house the whole 20 years in Tucson, and

I became a really good long distance swimmer. I do about 100 laps a day, then I finish off with some tricks, including doing ten underwater back flips and then 20 underwater front flips. Only one breath on each one. It's awesome, man! Blows people away.

We all liked the new digs, I think because it was so different and like an adventure. I never saw so many cool animals in my life. We once had a mountain lion go to sleep on our side porch, leaning right up against the sliding glass door. I tried to open the door to let him in to play, and my mom screamed at me louder than she ever did in her entire life. We had lots of things called scorpions, which apparently bite you and it really hurts. One of them bit my dad on the ass, and he couldn't sit down for a couple of days. None of them ever bit me, so I thought they were kinda cute. My mom spent at least part of the day screaming whenever we found scorpions around the house, which was pretty much everyday. Me and my dad laughed at her, except after my dad got bit on the ass—he didn't laugh for those couple of days. The best were the tarantulas—we were like the central bus station for these things my dad says are called 'Mexican blonde tarantulas'—big mothers almost the size of a dinner plate when they spread their legs out. They don't bite you as long as you don't bother them. Sometimes when we came home from somewhere, there would be like 5 or 6 tarantulas on our front door, and we would just walk around and go in the back door so as not to disturb them. Even my mom liked watching them, but not when they got in the house. A couple of times they got into my parents bed at night and my mom would yell (but not as loud as with scorpions) and make my dad catch 'em and take them outside. But we always took special care to make sure we didn't hurt them. And there were lots of other animals that passed through our yard, which was a whole new experience. My mom grew up in the country and knew a lot about animals and she even hunted animals as a kid. So she knew a lot more about any animals than my dad, who grew up around NYC. My mom says that my dad thinks a poodle off a leash is a form of wildlife–I think she is making fun of him. But we had deer, bobcats, these really weird animals called coatimundis, javelinas (they look like wild pigs but aren't pigs at all–I learned that at the Desert Museum), lots of birds like quail and doves and hawks. And some big snakes–sometimes even rattlesnakes! They have Gila monsters here, which are poisonous and scary looking and everyone said they were never around and we would never see one, but we ended up having a whole family of them in our garage and had to call some people to remove them to live somewhere else. Mostly, all the animals left us alone and for me, it was the craziest place I ever lived and very exciting. One time, my mom and I went down the driveway to get our empty trash can after pick-up day, and there was a big javelina on the side of the driveway that started making noise and showed its teeth and snarled at us. The hair on its back went straight up. It looked pissed off and then my mom looked on the other side of the driveway and there were two baby javelinas. My mom told me later that was a real bad thing to do–to get between the babies and the mama javelina. It started to charge at us and my mom threw the empty garbage can at it, grabbed my arm and we ran like hell, but it only chased us a little bit and went back to its babies. And those are the only good animal stories I can tell you in my entire life, cause I was a city guy my whole life. A couple of years later, we moved to the central part of Tucson and we never saw much in the way of animals except cool birds, a few coyotes, and one javelina that must have gotten lost. We moved cause we spent so much time driving back and forth between the house and downtown Tucson and the university area, that it seemed stupid to live so far up there. Except for my dad hiking a little, we just didn't do much up in the foothills, though it was pretty, especially watching lightning storms come over the valley–I bet you didn't know that Tucson gets more lightning than almost any other place in the whole country. But I get to see the lightning up close even now. I missed the animals a little, but we all liked it better downtown. Still got a nice house with a pool and a basketball hoop. And my cable TV, computer, and 3 different video systems. And my stereo speakers. So I am pretty much covered. My parents say I am spoiled.

We had a short period of arguing a little while after we moved to Tucson, because I decided to retire. Just didn't feel like working anymore. Part of it was that I didn't know people like I did in Philly and part of it was I had too much other stuff to do. So my dad sat me down and gave me a long lecture on why I needed to work and why it was good for me. I really didn't pay much attention. I just said no way. Finally my mom asked my dad if he would like to retire and he said, "Sure, but somebody's got to pay the bills." And then my mom said, "That would be you. So leave him alone and if he changes his mind, he can work anytime he wants." That was the end of my working career. My mom is much smarter than my dad.

But my parents wanted me to get into the social scene of Tucson and arranged to have some 'social companions' for me to cruise around with. They didn't want me to have to hang around with just them, and I think they wanted a little time to themselves as well. It wasn't like hanging out with Monica, who I already told you lived in our Philly building for a while and was like my sister. They were usually students at the U of A (that's the University of Arizona). And they were always girls, cause I already told you that girls are the best people to hang out with. I became friends with several girls from the U of A, but none like Valerie, who was from Chicago, and was sort of a hippie, but not like a hippie in the old days. My parents said she was real smart and knew exactly how to help me fit in and they were right.

Valerie took me everywhere when we went out, usually Friday or Saturday nights and we always hung out with her friends. We went to parties at friends' houses, college parties, bowling, bars, music clubs, movies, you name it. Valerie just took me along everywhere and I became good friends with her good friends. And they all watched out for me. In fact, here is a funny story. My dad and I were in a big store buying me some DVD's. He went off to look for some music CD's and I stayed in the wrestling DVD section to pick a few out. When he came back, he found me talking to a stranger who had his arms around my shoulders and was tickling me. And we were play boxing too. He was a young dude, with long hair and a beard, sort of like my dad, but a LOT younger. Anyway, my dad thought I was breaking one of the big rules: NO TALKING TO STRANGERS. So he runs up and yells at the guy to leave me alone and get his hands off me. And the guy (his name was Tom) yells back at my dad and says, "Who the fuck are you? I happen to be one of Shane's friends." Well, I thought they were going to get in a fistfight or something, until my dad said, "I'm his fucking father." And then Tom smiled and said sorry and apologized. See, my dad thought he was protecting me from Tom, and Tom thought he was protecting me from my dad, who I already told you looks like a homeless guy, not that there is anything wrong with homeless people. I was really good friends with lots of homeless people in Old City, after all. And then Tom and I explained to my dad that Tom was one of my best friends through Valerie and that I had been to his house several times for parties and to hang out, and we went to some music clubs for dancing, movies, and that sort of stuff. Then my dad apologized too, and we went and had some sodas and everyone was cool about the whole thing.

I don't think my parents realized how much stuff I did with Valerie until one Saturday night on 4th Avenue. Now

4th Avenue in Tucson is like a hippy place with college kids around too. A little bit like Dinkytown in Minneapolis. Lots of funky places, music and bars. Turned out that this night, my parents were hanging out on 4th Avenue and they didn't know I was, too. They walked by Berky's Bar (it's gone now) and looked in the open doors cause there was loud music playing and people were dancing and drinking. Their mouths were open when they saw me in the middle of the floor dancing with one of Val's girlfriends. I was holding a cue stick, cause I was also in the middle of a big pool game. They slowly walked in and saw Valerie, who waved and smiled but kept talking to her friends cause she knew I was OK and this is what we did at night. They came over to me and slapped me five and asked how I was doin' and I said fine. Then I asked them to hand me my drink off the bar, cause I was sweaty and hot from all that dancing and the crowded place. I pointed to my glass of milk on the bar and they handed it to me and I guzzled it in one gulp. I didn't drink alcohol then, but I do now. Anyway, they just smiled and waved to the gang who waved back at them, and left. When we all ended up back home that night, my mom said it seemed that I had a much better time on Saturday nights than they did. And my dad simply said, "It sucks getting old, Shano."

Chapter 2
Motorcycling and the Police

One of the absolute best things that happened after moving to Tucson was motorcycling. My dad had a small bike for a while in Philly when we lived in the shithole town on the Main Line, and we rode a little, but there was no place we really wanted to ride to. My dad said riding in the city of Philadelphia was a 'death wish', so when we moved into Old City, he got rid of that bike. And he pretty much forgot about motorcycles for a long time. Shortly after we got to Tucson, my mom noticed a lot of people riding motorcycles. As I told you, my dad is really absent-minded and doesn't really notice anything. So one day my mom says to my dad, "Isn't this supposed to be a great place to ride motorcycles? Seems to me all the motorcycle commercials always have people riding around the Southwest. And I'm seeing a lot of people on motorcycles." My dad thought about that for about 5 seconds and said, "You're right. This is a great place to ride motorcycles." So he asked me, "Shano, will you ride with me if I get another bike?" I said sure I would, and within a few weeks we had the first of about 8 motorcycles that we ended up getting. We've calculated it out, and I have over 50,000 miles as a passenger riding with my dad. In fact, he will hardly ever ride with anyone else on the back of his motorcycles, cause he is so used to me and I am so used to him. He says I ride perfectly relaxed and always know exactly how to lean just a little in turns, like a pro. I've seen him have someone else on his bike when we ride with friends, and he'll make most of them get off, cause he says they don't know what they are doing and are going to cause an accident. And I love to go fast–I hate when anyone passes us and scream at him when he lets that happen, but he only laughs. But he likes to go fast, too, which is the great thing about riding in the desert. The roads are empty and you can go really fast. I mean like 150 mph fast if you want, though we only did that once, and when I broke my promise to my dad and bragged about that to my mom, my dad almost had his bikes taken away. My dad's great friend from Philly, Patrick, once rode on the back of a bike with my dad during a visit, and Patrick used to ride a lot when he was younger and lived in Ireland. After his ride, he told my dad he was smiling for 20% of the ride, which is only a small part of the ride. My dad asked him what he was doing the other 80% of the time, and Patrick said, "I was screaming." But make no mistake, we are very safe riders–we wear all our safety gear–helmets, armored jackets, big gloves, boots, everything. We look cool. I look particularly cool because I like my stuff to match–so if I wear a red helmet, I gotta have red gloves and a red jacket. Same goes for yellow. My dad doesn't give a shit and will wear whatever he happens to put on and doesn't look nearly as cool as me. He just doesn't get it at all.

I think the greatest thing that happened because of our motorcycling was meeting Kathleen and Kyle, who became our best friends in Tucson. And their son, Bobby, who also rode with us a lot when he was young, but now he is grown up and doesn't ride with us much, but I see him a lot anyway when we go out to eat and stuff. Kathleen was a doc with my dad and one day they discovered that they both liked riding. So we met up one Sunday and headed out to Tombstone, where they have cowboys and shootouts and everything. Pretty nice ride, but sort of straight roads which aren't as much fun. But Kathleen and Kyle had big Harley-Davidson motorcycles, cause Kyle is a top-notch motorcycle mechanic for the Harley-Davidson Company. I love those bikes. My dad never got one of those and though we rode cruisers sometimes (which were like H-D motorcycles, only made in Japan), he rode other bikes like Aprilias, Hondas, Kawasakis and BMW motorcycles. Some of them we could ride on dirt roads, some just looked pretty and fast, and one was something called a Superbike, which even scared me a little cause it could go fast like in one second with the front wheel off the ground–but I loved it. He only let me ride with him on that a few times, cause he said it was too fast for two people and the rear seat sucked, which I can tell you is entirely true. He got rid of that bike after only a couple of years cause he said he was going to either kill himself or go to jail for speeding.

So pretty quickly, we were riding almost every weekend with Kyle and Kathleen and Bobby to all sorts of places. Our all-time favorite ride was/is to Arivaca, Arizona. It's about 140 miles round trip from our house and we go there for a cup of coffee and either a piece of pie or quiche, to the Gadsden Coffee Company, and their little cafe called Cafe Aribac. The first reason we love to go there is to ride on Arivaca Road, which is about 25 miles each way. It has lots of really tight curves and loops and is unbelievably exciting to ride fast, but not too fast, because every year a couple of people get killed on that road. We do it very carefully but pretty fast. But not the fastest–sometimes really fast riders pass us, but we don't care. It's a very popular motorcycle road and you get to wave to lots of bikers. But the really cool thing is when you get to Cafe Aribac. It's the coolest cafe ever. It sits in the middle of nowhere with cows and horses around sometimes, with great views over the mountains and grasslands all around. But it's the people, man, the people. Tom Shook owned it but he 'passed away' and now his brother Joe owns it along with Brad, the roastmaster, cause they roast their own coffee which everyone thinks is the best coffee you can ever get. I don't drink coffee, but I'll take their word for it. Joe and Brad are great guys and friends and so are all the people who have worked there–like Robin, Janet, Mike, Bonnie, and Austin and Colin (they didn't work there much, they are Joe's sons). The customers are so cool cause they are all so different. There are lots of REAL hippies who live around there, lots of great townspeople from Arivaca, cowboys who still wear their guns (and once in awhile ride to the cafe on their horses), all types of motorcyclists (including racers and gangs), birdwatchers cause it is a famous bird watching area, bicyclists, you name it. It's the wildest group of people you ever saw going to meet in one place in your life. And I've made a lot of friends there over the years, cause we are regulars and everyone knows exactly what I eat and drink the second I arrive. Almost everyone at the tables say hi to me when we get there, cause they know us. And motorcyclists are always friendly to each other–it's like a big club for everyone. So, on many weekends, our little group rides out there. But we also go to places like Patagonia and Tombstone and Bisbee and Kitt Peak and other places too, cause there are so many great day rides and destinations (my dad's word).

Even though I am a great motorcycling riding partner, I have made some mistakes. The one that pissed off my dad the most occurred right off Arivaca Road. We pulled over for my dad to go pee in the bushes, but he had to walk like 20 yards cause that's where the bushes were. You need to understand what it's like out there. It's a lot of desert and nothing else. And there are 'migrants' (I don't really know that word) out there that are always in the news and we've bumped into a few over the years and generally they run away. A couple of times, we met a few couples from Mexico who didn't speak English and asked us for water, and we always gave them our water to drink, since we could always refill our bottles later–they seemed very thirsty and were always very polite and thanked us. Anyway, there's a lot of special police cars riding all around our part of Arizona because of the migrants. They are called the Border Patrol. There's Border Patrol trucks all over the place but they don't really care if you are motorcycling too fast, cause all they care about is looking for migrants.

Anyway, my dad was taking a long time peeing or whatever, and I was standing off the side of the road with our bike, when a Border Patrol truck came by, and I waved hello to them. They pulled over right away, I think because we were pulled over to the side of the road and they thought I was asking for help, not saying hello. They came toward me and asked if everything was OK. I had my helmet and shades on, so they couldn't even tell I was a Downer. I just put up my finger to my helmet and made the sign for "shush" (that means keep quiet) and pointed toward the bushes where my dad was peeing, though he was certainly taking his time. Next thing you know, these two guys got their guns out and slowly crept towards the bushes. Seemed sort of crazy to me, but, hey, that's their job. Almost immediately, my dad started coming out of the bushes, and they screamed at him to put his hands up. Pretty sure they scared the crap out of him, if he was just peeing. It only lasted a few seconds, cause they quickly saw my dad had his motorcycle gear on, and he yelled out that he was only peeing in the bushes. Then we all got together and they figured out what had happened and everyone had a great laugh, except my dad, who faked his laugh. After the cops left, he did his usual, "Don't ever do that again."

Which is exactly what my mom said to me a few months later at Tucson Airport when we were flying somewhere–I think it was to Vegas. She had to go to the ladies room and told me to sit along the wall outside the restroom door and stay put, and that she would be back in a second. Well, she took too long for my tastes, so when the police walked by, I asked them to go check on my mom since I was worried we might miss our plane if she stayed in there much longer. It was two guy cops and they understood me pretty well. They yelled into the bathroom and waited a minute till the one or two women in there were gone and it was just my mom, I guess. Then they went in and my mom said she was in the toilet and one of the cops said, "Is Shane's mom in here?" Apparently, my mom didn't want to have a conversation on the toilet with the police, but she had no choice. "Yes. Is there a problem with Shane?" And they said, "No ma'am, Shane's outside and he is fine but he said he was worried about you and that we needed to check to see if you are OK. Are you OK, ma'am?" Now I don't think I actually said all that, but that's what they took away from my conversation with them. And my mom said (I was listening at the door now), "I'm fine."

"Are you sure ma'am. Shane seems worried."

"Yes, I just have to go to the bathroom."

"Do you need any assistance, ma'am?"

"No, I am peeing. I don't need help to do that."

"You don't need to get upset, ma'am. Shane was just worried about you."

"You can leave now. I don't need any help. Tell him I will be out in a minute."

Now my mom, for some reason, didn't think it was particularly funny that I sent the police into the ladies room to check on her. I thought it was pretty funny, myself. The cops were great guys and they hung out with me for a few minutes until my mom came out to make sure everything was OK. My mom looked pissed and just when she thought those guys were too far away to hear us, she said that same thing, like my dad, "Shane, don't ever do that again." Then the cops came back and politely told my mom that I was only trying to be nice and take care of her and that she shouldn't be mad at me. And they both patted me on the back and said I was a good guy. My mom didn't yell at me at all, but it was another ten or fifteen minutes before she calmed down. My parents are so sensitive when I try to be helpful.

Chapter 3
Marrying K & K and Coney Island

OK, I'll admit it. I fell in love with Kathleen. She is the coolest woman I ever met and I decided to become her second husband, after Kyle. Which she agreed to. I don't really know what that means, but no matter, we both called each other husband and wife and still do, wherever we go together. Unfortunately, I don't get to live and sleep with her. Kyle was completely cool with it. Which is pretty funny, cause I performed their marriage ceremony.

See, when we first met, they weren't married and then later they decided to get married. And Kathleen asked what the rules were for getting married in Arizona and no one knew. She wanted some friend or someone to come from some other part of the country to marry them, but no one knew the rules. My dad started checking into the laws and even called his buddy, Jamie, across the street, who is a law professor. Turns out this is the rule and my dad has to write it for me: "If either of the people getting married believe the person performing a marriage is qualified to perform a marriage, then the marriage is lawful, even if the person isn't qualified to perform a marriage." Sounds ridiculous, doesn't it–but it's true. Yeah, makes no sense, but it's from the 1800's I think, and my dad says it's probably cause some people got married by fake judges and fake clergy and stuff and no one wanted to find out that their marriages were no good, so that's the law, even today. Well, Kathleen and Kyle both agreed that they 'believed' I was qualified to perform their marriage. So one Sunday, a whole bunch of us went to one of our favorite bars in Tucson and I performed the marriage ceremony. There happened to be a judge there who offered to do it, but when we told him what we knew, he said that was correct and he let me finish. I got a little pissed when I thought he was going to push his way in, but fortunately he backed down. I really didn't know the words you were supposed to say, but since I also believed I was qualified to perform a marriage, it didn't matter. And my final words cracked everyone up, cause instead of saying, 'May you live in health and happiness until death do you part', I said, "May you live in hell, till death do you part." Which was not a mistake, I really did think those were the correct words. Anyway, it was a great party and how many people can say they married two of their best friends without knowing what the hell they were saying. And it was legal.

My wife, Kathleen and I took our delayed honeymoon to NYC a few years later. Unfortunately, my mom accompanied us. We had a suite with two queen beds and sadly, I had to share the bed with my mom instead of Kathleen. Though she did get drunk a couple of nights and I could have snuck into her bed, but that wouldn't have been very polite. We all shared a very intimate suite at the 57th Street Holiday Inn, which is the greatest hotel in NYC. And I've stayed at really swanky NY hotels–I'm talking some of the best 5 star hotels–but they are all just pretentious crap (my mom's words) compared to the 57th Street Holiday Inn. Cause at that Holiday Inn, I met the owner of the whole hotel (he owns others too–he's a cool guy) on the very first night in the bar area, and he immediately took a liking to me and my mom and treated us like royalty.

We were all in town for a very special event, the Coney Island Mermaid Parade. Google it–it's the coolest thing in the world. Better than the Mummers Parade in Philly by a long shot. See, my mom's best friend in NY is Marie Roberts and she is the banner painter for all of Coney Island (she's an art professor, too) and is famous and is sometimes on TV specials about Coney Island and art. She's also one of my best friends, too, and painted huge banner paintings of all of us that are hanging in our house. She painted me as the Strong Man–it's very cool. One day while we were there, Marie spent the whole day with me and I got to meet all the freaks and performers in the Coney Island Freak Show–you know, the fire-eater, the strong man, the sword swallower, the contortionist, the guy who puts nails up his nose (great guy), and Serpentina, the snake lady, who is a great friend of my mom's as well.

Marie got all three of us named as judges at the Mermaid Parade. Which means you get to sit in a grandstand with a whole bunch of other judges and get to watch these crazy people perform music and marches and dances and twirling and dressing up in strange clothes, and sometimes taking off all their clothes, and a lot more crazy stuff, in order to win the grand prize as the best act in the parade. One of the important rules is that anything goes and that means the judges can be bribed–it actually means the judges have to be bribed. So we all got great gifts, which included fancy T-shirts, fancy cakes and desserts, bottles of booze, and that sort of stuff in order that we voted for them. We got a lot of bottles of booze and since we were traveling from Arizona, it was too much to carry. Well, the judges stand was protected by the NYPD, and some of them were on motorcycles which really attracted me to them and I started to get friendly with those guys. Once I had a few bottles of booze, my mom told me to take them over and give them to the cops. They laughed and said they were on duty and couldn't touch them. But one cool cop named Tony said his saddlebag was open and it was OK if I put a bottle in his saddlebag without him knowing, which I did. Next thing you know there was about 5 more motorcycle cops that pulled up next to him, and I just kept bringing down bottles of booze that either we or some other judge didn't want (we got way too many bribes to carry) and put them in all their saddlebags. Boy, did they like me!!

There were famous people at that parade. The Grand Marshall was a famous actor named Harvey Keitel, and his wife was really nice, too. He kept asking to have his picture taken with me cause I think he was jealous that people were paying more attention to me than him. I was really hamming it up and having a great old time and everyone was hanging out with me more than him. Not that I am famous or anything, just fun to hang with. My mom said that at one point he said, "Why the hell did they make me Grand Marshall, it should have been Shano." He just didn't understand that I have no interest in having my picture taken with men. Only women. And my favorite woman that day was Jennifer, the bearded lady at Coney Island. I just couldn't figure out that whole bearded lady thing at all. It still is very confusing to me. Jennifer is terrific and kept letting me rub her beard and then her breasts and explaining that you could have both these things and still be a girl, but I think the whole thing is just crazy. But Jennifer was about as cool a person as can be and we became friends in an instant. I don't know who actually won the Parade contest, but I didn't really care and I don't think many other people did, since everyone just had a great time, especially at the Mermaid Ball that night.

Oh, I forgot to mention a few things that the owner of the Holiday Inn did for us. Coney Island is a long ride from

57th Street, so he had a big white limousine ready for us the morning of the parade. To take us to and from Coney Island. My mom told him we couldn't do that cause we had to meet friends and go there as a group. And he said, fine, the limousine would pick up everyone and drop them off home that night–it was ours for the day. What a guy! We had about 10 people in that limo and for free! My mom even tried to tip the driver who said he couldn't take the tip cause if the hotel owner found out, he would cut his hand off. I think he was kidding. My mom didn't think he was kidding. Whenever we were at the hotel bar, we got food and drinks sent over to us all night long from this great woman bartender who became our friend. And get this, we weren't allowed to pay for anything there either!! And just about everyone who worked there learned my name and treated us very special, like we were really important people. And I'm talking everyone – the bellhops, the maids, the doormen, the drivers, the waiters, the people at the front desk, I mean everyone. Just because the owner and all those people who worked there really liked me and my mom. And Kathleen, of course.

The night before the parade, we took the free limousine out to Coney Island for a special circus show. It was sold out, but my mom's friend, Trish, got us front row seats so I could see everything real close. I got so excited waiting for it to start and then suddenly some famous politician I never heard of showed up with some really big guys and they said we had to move, cause the guy was so fucking important. Big deal–we had our tickets. Fortunately, Trish didn't take shit from anyone and pulled out her cellphone and started taking a movie of them trying to throw me and us out of our seats so he could sit there with his bodyguards or whatever. Trish started yelling she was going to send this to a TV station and put it on YouTube and that guy backed down pretty quick. He sat close to us, but his bodyguards didn't get to take our seats–they had to stand way back. Then the guy tried to be buddies with me and have his picture taken with me and I said no fucking way, cause even though I don't really know what it was all about, I did know he tried to take my seat. To me, that's like trying to take my ball away from me in the playground, and we all know where that leads to. Anyway, we ignored him and had a great time at the circus. The motorcycles in the round cage were the best thing, by the way.

Chapter 4
Visitors and Vegas

One of the great things about Tucson is that it's warm in the winter, so lots of people come to visit us all the time, especially when they have snow and want to get away. It's hot here in the summer, but we've been here so long that we all like summer better than winter, cause everything is less crowded and it becomes real quiet in town and there's no crowds or waiting at restaurants and stuff like that. And we all love to hang out in the pool, especially me.

Matt and his family have come out lots of times, and sometimes just Matt comes out to see me on his own. My parents just shake their heads when we take off on a Friday or Saturday night (in my dad's car!) to hit the bars or go to his old frat house (it's got the same name as the one he belonged to at Syracuse where he went to college). We have a great time and meet incredible numbers of women who give us their phone numbers (well, mostly to Matt). Matt says I am better to take to a bar or party than taking a puppy to the beach, to meet women at least. Which I take as a compliment, since the babes are all attracted to me first, and then Matt makes his moves. It's hysterical. We have a real routine we do.

One summer, his whole family came out and stayed at a fancy resort called Loews Ventana Canyon and the place was empty cause it was hotter than hell as usual. We had the whole place almost to ourselves. And we definitely had the whole big pool there to ourselves. So we set up a big pool basketball game with my dad and Paul as captains, and all the kids got split up on each team. The loser (Paul or my dad) had to pay for dinner, which was like a couple of hundred bucks for so many people, so this was a serious game. I'll cut this short. As the game came to a close, it was tied, just like my famous kickball game. Next shot that went in was going to be the winner. My dad and Paul started acting real serious–though I don't think they cared that much who actually paid for dinner–it was just a bet for fun and they are very competitive. Then again, there was no smiling at this point. I was on Paul's team with Matt, and we started passing the ball around far from the basket looking to go inside. I don't know what the hell I was thinking, but I was like 30 feet from the basket and everyone started yelling at me to pass the ball. I got confused a bit and decided I would just end it. So I started to shoot the ball and my whole team was screaming, "Shano, don't shoot the ball!" Well, I shot it, and it went in, and we won the game, and then everyone (except my dad, who just lost a couple of hundred bucks) was jumping all over me for hitting that shot and winning the damn game. I think I've seen Coach Dunphy have a look like that sometimes during Temple games, when someone takes a really long shot and he starts shaking his head like that was a really bad shot to take, but if it goes in, he claps hard. This was the same thing. And at the end, even my dad was smiling, too.

Goitse has come to Tucson several times. That's not really visitors, but it is to me. That's the name of the Irish band that Conal (remember, Patrick's son and my buddy from Philly and now Ireland) is in, and they play at either big auditoriums or sometimes clubs in Tucson when they pass through. They travel all around the world to play Irish music and are pretty famous. Sometimes they even go to China and Japan, and other very faraway places. The first time they played in Tucson at a big auditorium, right in the middle of the concert, Conal walked up to the microphone and said the next song was for his good friend Shano, and had me stand up and bow to the whole audience. That was pretty special. But then I met the fiddler in the band. Her name is Aine and she is beautiful and sings beautifully and plays the fiddle great. I told Conal thanks for saying my name, but said next time, it would be better to have Aine do it, cause she is a helluva lot prettier than Conal. And next time they came, sure enough, Aine dedicated a love song to me, and that was even more special, because I have a crush on her. No offense to Conal–he's a great friend since my 21st birthday party, but that's just the facts of life. His brother, Brendan, is also a good friend and lived in China for years and we used to FaceTime with him and his wife and their cats (which make strange sounds like they are talking) all the time. He's like a genius Chinese scholar (according to my dad), but they moved to Philly recently, so we can just call them on the phone now. Conal and Brendan are great guys.

I, myself, had a brief stint in the entertainment field. It was a one shot affair, but I had the crowd roaring and clapping along with me. It was during a trip to Vegas. My parents hate Las Vegas, but they are culturally very backward and don't appreciate the finer places like Disneyland, Disney World, Six Flags, and other important places of fun. But they have always forced themselves to take me to those places since I love that stuff. My mom flew with me to Vegas and we met some friends to have a good time, which we did. It started off pretty good, cause I was hot on the slots and made about $100 the first day. The slots are pretty much the only thing I play since I don't understand the rules of the other games. Apparently, lots of people are like that, since the slot machines were always full everywhere we went. I'm not bragging, but I was the only person among us who won almost every day and I came home with over $200 dollars in my pockets playing slots. I made my mom take me to every major casino on the Strip and it was great.

Another of the really cool things in Vegas is that there are guys standing on almost every street corner handing out cards with pictures of naked women on them. At first, no one would give me any cards at all. Once they saw I was a handicapper, they turned away. I asked my mom about it, and I was happy to see that she thought that was wrong. Even though she didn't particularly like the naked girls on the cards. This is called a 'moral dilemma' according to my dad, who wasn't with us on that quick trip. So she went up to the next guy handing out cards and told him to give me a card. He said he couldn't, cause I was too young. Well, we were ready for that, since I always looked younger than I was my whole life and I had my picture ID with me that whole trip, mostly for gambling purposes. And I was plenty old enough. So we showed him the ID and he gave me a card. My mom asked him to give me some more. And then she made sure I got cards at every corner all the time. By the time we left Vegas, I had a big stack. At first, I thought they were pretty cool, but after awhile, it's the same old thing, and let's face it, they aren't anywhere near as good as baseball or wrestling cards, so I just threw them away.

There's this big thing that people talk about all the time and it's called sex. Now I like sexy women just as much as the next guy. I recently found a video while I was cruising on the Internet of two naked women kissing and putting whipped cream all over themselves. It was pretty hot. So I brought my Chromebook out of my room to show my mom and dad, who laughed and didn't pay much attention, other than to say, "Knock yourself out, Shano." I expected a bigger reaction, but after a few more minutes, I realized that they were right, it wasn't that big a deal and I lost interest and moved on to some other videos. Which is not to say I don't sometimes watch hot babe videos. It just isn't sports or wrestling. Or even a good movie.

Now what was I talking about? Oh yeah, my one moment of glory on the stage. My mom and I were in some big casino and it was during something called "Carnival Week", which is when everyone dresses up in funny outfits, and bands play great music and mostly, everyone is dancing. The showgirls and all the other dancers were up on a stage and then wandering off the stage and into the crowd and getting people to dance with them and just grooving to the music. I couldn't keep my feet still, cause as I already told you, I can dance with the best of them. Next thing you know, I lost my mom and couldn't find her anywhere. So I went with this gorgeous woman who wasn't wearing much clothes and she danced with me all the way back on the stage. And then I did my 'shimmy-shake' move and quite a few others until I ended up in the middle of the stage surrounded by all the other dancers, who were clapping and hollering and watching me put on a real dance show. Then the crowd got into it, and they started clapping and dancing to the music and following my lead. I was the star of the show for about 3 minutes or so. I think I could have taken over the whole stage cause I had them in 'the palm of my hand', so to speak. Unfortunately, my mom had freaked out when she lost me, called security and everyone was searching for me pretty quick. She was panicking and was almost crying when she says she looked up and to her surprise, saw me in the middle of the stage, dancing my ass off. She let me go another few minutes or so, and then had them get me back down on the floor. Some guy from the show came down to talk to us and said I was so good and that the crowd liked me so much, that they wanted me to come back the next day and do it again. But my mom said we had other plans and couldn't, which was a bummer. I asked her why I couldn't do it, and she replied, "Shane, they are just trying to exploit you." I have no clue what that means. But she was so relieved to find me and thought I was so good dancing on the stage, that I didn't even get a "Don't do that ever again."

One of the big things in Vegas is going to the shows. They have all kinds of shows that are pretty neat, but you have to get your tickets to them way before you actually go to Vegas, cause they get sold out months before you get there, which makes no sense to me. You'd think they would just add more seats. And naturally, my mom didn't know anything about this, so we had no seats to anything at all. I said I wanted to see a magic show and she checked it out and found some show with a guy named Lance Burton, who everyone said was great. And we went to that casino and walked up to the box office to buy tickets. The guy said it was sold out, and my mom asked for tickets for the next night, and he said it was sold out for quite awhile, long after we were going home. I was OK with that, since I never heard of the guy before and figured we'd just go to some other show–I didn't care as long as we did something. So my mom and me stepped off to the side and started looking at some visitor's guide for another show. Meanwhile, I was getting really hungry for lunch and started bugging my mom that we needed to eat soon or I was going to pass out. That's my general line when I am really hungry. Finally, she said, "Enough, Shane, we'll find a place to go soon. Just calm down and wait a minute until I figure out another show to go to."

Well, the ticket guy was watching us and could only hear part of what we were saying, but he thought I was very disappointed at not seeing Lance Burton. I was actually pissed because my mom was delaying lunch and I was damn hungry. But then he called us back to his desk and asked us to wait a few minutes. He was going to make a call. And ten minutes later, we had tickets. For free–something called 'complimentary', which simply means they like you and it's a gift. When we went to the show that night, we sat at something called 'the producers table'. Which is for really important people, I think, since it's the front row, and they bring you free food and drinks, and the people in the show even come right by your table. A few of the showgirls even SAT at our table and were very nice to me and a couple of them kissed me on the cheek and people clapped. I never heard people clap about some guy getting kissed on the cheek, but I didn't care–these were hot babes. They even took our picture and gave us copies for free. Really great folks. And this is not a commercial or anything, but that guy Burton was awesome.

Well, my mom is no dummy. She noticed there was another front row table right next to ours and it was empty. When we got back to our hotel that night, she had this funny look on her face and simply said, "Tomorrow, Shane, we are going to get more tickets to shows." And then she smiled a real big smile and said, "Shane, tomorrow, we are going to exploit you." I wish people wouldn't keep repeating big words they know I don't understand.

So we went to another casino to get tickets to a music show–sort of a rock concert with some guy named Rick Springfield. Sold out. My mom took me aside again but just so the ticket seller could still see us and whispered to me that I needed to look real sad, and if possible cry a little. I said I couldn't just cry for no reason, but I was able to give my best sad look. So I did that, and my mom kept trying to hide her smile, keeping her back to the ticket guy, while she waited to see what happened. In a couple of minutes, pretty much the same thing happened as the day before. He called us back, made a call, and boom, that night we were at another 'producers table', getting free food and drinks, hanging with showgirls and everything. People in the crowd thought we were celebrities or something.

We did this two more times successfully, and I got to see the magicians with the lions and tigers just a few weeks before one of the lions tried to eat one of the magicians and they never did their act again, so that was a good break for me, though I felt sorry for the guy who got bit by the lion or tiger or whatever. Later, when my mom read about that guy getting attacked, she almost fainted, cause we were sitting so close to those lions and tigers on the stage that they were breathing on us. They could have jumped on us in a second, though we never even thought about it. Had no idea those big cats could lose it and eat you. I think that was a close call we didn't even know about.

Chapter 5
Truck stops and Art galleries

Art is very important to my mom. She really loves it. And so do I. I am a pretty good photographer and carry my camera with me wherever I go. I think I told you my specialties are tattoos on women, public bathrooms and sunsets. And a few other things thrown in. Almost every sunset at our house, I take a picture of it. I have thousands of pictures from the same spot with the sun going down. A lot of them suck, but some of them are spectacular. My mom was going to try to arrange a photography show for me once, but we never got around to it. Maybe one day.

Now bathrooms in restaurants are pretty interesting places. They often have framed pictures and flowers and mirrors, not to mention the sinks and toilets. So I generally take a few shots of bathrooms whenever I go out to eat and some of them come out pretty funny. Once, my mom saw me talking on the phone with some woman I called. I got her number and name from one of my pictures I took at the TTT, which is the Tucson Truck Terminal. You can laugh if you want, but that's where Omar's Hi-Way Chef Restaurant is. And my dad says it was named the second best truck stop restaurant in the whole US for several years. We like going there for breakfast in the afternoon, cause they make pancakes and waffles all day long. And Omar is this really big friendly guy who always remembers me and is very nice to me like almost everyone in Tucson is. We all think Tucson is the friendliest town we have ever lived in.

Anyway, I was on the phone with this lady who couldn't understand anything I was saying. My mom asked who I was talking to, cause I think she thought one of our friends had called and I was just chatting like I always do. But since I couldn't understand the lady either, I just handed the phone to my mom. The lady asked who we were and why I called her and my mom asked her to hold on for a second. She turned to me and asked, "Shane, where did you get this lady's number?" And I showed her my camera, which had a very respectable picture of the men's bathroom at Omar's Hi-Way Restaurant. And you could see very clearly on the wall (when you enlarged it), that lady's name and telephone number right on the wall. With some other writing on it. My mom laughed quietly and got back on the phone.

"Umm, the person who called is my son and as I'm sure you noticed, he has a speech impediment and is difficult to understand. He is handicapped and I apologize for him bothering you."

"Yes, but he knew my name was Mary and he had my phone number. How did he get that?"

See, I could read and say Mary, since Mary was like one of my sisters in Miami–remember? I can sight read hundreds of words, by the way.

My mom looked a little confused, but finally she just replied, "I'm sorry to say that he took a picture of the bathroom wall in the men's room at the TTT and your name and number is on it."

I heard the woman scream over the phone even though I was about ten feet from my mom.

My mom said she was horrified–that means very upset. And then she asked my mom if there was anything my mom could do to get it taken off, but my mom told her she couldn't exactly go into that men's room to wash it off. Then my mom told her not to worry, because there were a lot of other women's names on the wall, too. Apparently, this didn't cheer the lady up.

Afterwards, my mom called my dad at work and told him the story, and I heard him laugh over the phone just about as loud as when that woman screamed.

• • •

Obviously, one of the big reasons I like photography and all art is cause of my mom, who always encouraged me to do art, though I suck at everything except photography. But I am very good at art gallery openings. I've flown from Tucson to NY for openings several times. I've been to probably a hundred art openings (when you add in all my years in Philly) and maybe a lot more, since there were lots of art galleries in Old City by the time we moved and I knew all the owners. And I went to my mom's openings in NYC and we would go to other art openings of my mom's friends. So I am pretty experienced at art openings. Being good at art openings is pretty easy once you realize what is supposed to happen. You're supposed to look at the paintings or sculptures or photographs and look at them a while, and then when someone comes by and looks with you, you have a talk about what it means to you. I can't do that, since only close friends can understand what I'm saying–I know– I keep repeating that, but that's the way it is. But I found that when someone comes by, I could point to something in the painting or whatever, and the person would usually ask me if I liked it and then THEY would start talking about the piece, telling me what they thought it was about. And point things out to me. Most of the time they were full of shit. At least that's what my mom and dad said, but I loved doing the whole art scene. I always dressed up in my black silk shirt, black pants, black socks, and black shoes, cause that's what cool artsy people do–I watched carefully over the years and figured that out for myself. So I would stand there and listen to people tell me about the art and what it meant. Sometimes they would get uncomfortable with me if they didn't know me, and one time I just grabbed a woman standing nearby and brought her over to talk to a guy who was explaining the painting to me. I was ready to move on. I looked back and they talked at that painting for quite awhile. That's when I discovered my special gift at art openings. I realized I could stand at a painting until someone came over and started a short conversation of sorts. Then I would tell them to wait a minute and I'd go find someone who I could bring over to the painting for them to talk about it. It's called being a host, I think. I started realizing this was pretty cool. Especially since people at art openings are generally very nice, gentle people and would never just walk away from me–they were very polite to me. So at one of my mom's openings, I just spent the whole night walking around introducing people to each other and making them look at my mom's paintings and talking about them. My dad noticed this happening and thought it was really funny. Then he told me to stand at the door and greet everyone and thank them for coming, which I loved to do. I got the nickname 'glad-hand' by everyone. I was so good at getting people together at my mom's openings that a few artists asked her if they could hire me out for a job at their openings, but my mom and dad just laughed and said I had something called a 'restricted contract' and could only do her shows. But art openings are a lot of fun for a couple of hours. Then it's time to go out to dinner–enough is enough.

Chapter 6
My Tucson sports teams

You already know I'm a Temple sports guy. But I like lots of other teams, too, just not as much as Temple basketball. Since I live in Tucson, it's only natural that I like lots of University of Arizona teams. I used to love springtime, cause there used to be lots of major league spring training games in Tucson, but they all stay in Phoenix nowadays. And I was a big fan of the Tucson Toros and the Tucson Sidewinders, which were Triple-A minor league teams for many years, but they're gone from Tucson as well. I got to be great friends with one of the first basemen on the Sidewinders. His name was Steve Neal and after I got his autograph the first time, we just became buddies. We just clicked and I introduced him to my parents. He always gave me balls and bats after games and would wave to me during games–not while they were playing, but when he was running on or off the field. He and my mom and dad also became friends cause he was just the nicest guy you could imagine. We'd go out to eat with him and his wife and baby–lots of good times. And once again, we never would have known him if it wasn't for me. He made the Triple-A All-Star team and hit way over .300 and hit a lot of home runs. He was so close to getting to the majors and we all thought he never got a fair shot at it, cause there were some other Sidewinders who did get a shot and we thought he was better. My dad said the problem was that the Arizona Diamondbacks had too many good first basemen like Steve. Just bad luck, I guess. I saw him hit a double off Curt Schilling in an exhibition game–that's how good he was. And one game he asked and got permission for me to stand right next to him on first base at the opening of a game for the national anthem. I was the only guy on the field except the players–which was really cool. I really miss Steve a lot, cause he moved away. He was a real true friend.

• • •

OK, back to the University of Arizona, or the U of A, as everyone calls it. I like their basketball team pretty much and go to some of their games, but I've never talked to a player or coach. But they are really good and have lots of guys who play in the NBA. All the games are sold out in a really big arena called the McKale Center, but my dad's friends like Terry, Paul, Joe, and Becky always gave us tickets to games, since they've had them for many years, and they are great seats. About 5 rows up at center court. The games are a lot of fun, but it isn't nearly as loud as big Temple games, even though there are a lot more people there. That's because a lot of the fans are old people like my mom and dad and don't scream and yell like students. In fact, the student section is pretty small. It's a little weird, too, cause people don't go really crazy, either, like Temple or Madison Square Garden (I love that place) or the Palestra, which is another great place to watch Temple play basketball. In fact, at my very first game, I was sitting in that 5th row, and the ref made a really bad call against the U of A and I just stood up and called him a moron when he ran by and I made a nasty gesture with my arm, just like we sometimes did in the old days at McGonigle Hall. Well, everyone else was sitting down and they thought I was a complete nut and my dad quickly dragged me down into my seat and said I couldn't do that anymore. I asked why, and he just said I couldn't. No explanation. Very strange way to go to a game when you can't scream stuff at the ref. That's part of the fun of the game. Anyway, I like U of A basketball and I root for them always, except if they play one of the Philly teams, but that hardly ever happens. I don't think they have ever played Temple since we moved here.

I like U of A baseball games and women's softball and we go to those games too. But I LOVE the U of A women's volleyball team. We've been season ticketholders for years. Some years, the team comes in a van straight to my house and hand delivers our tickets right to our door. And we take pictures and get to know each other for the coming season. That's a really nice thing to do, don't you think? Those girls are great athletes, and it doesn't hurt that they are awfully pretty, too. I got to know lots of them over the years and even became friends with a few, including their parents, too. See, only a couple of thousand people go to those games, instead of like 15,000 at basketball, so you get to know lots of people at the games. I know the ticket guys, the security guys (Dave and Marty are my favorites), the camera guys–most of the folks who are there every year. Some of the parents of the players took a liking to me and would get me autographed volleyballs and T-shirts, and I have lots of pictures of me with the players and their parents. It's pretty cool to know them.

Chapter 7
The Grand Ending

Just like Philly, I could tell you tons more stories about my years in Tucson. But my dad says it's time to wrap this baby up. I asked him why, and he said enough is enough–we have lots of other stuff to do. He said it was more important to live life than to continuously write about it. I think we have gone way past his attention span, so I agreed.

He said I have to come up with some sort of grand philosophy of life to explain to all the readers. He also said I have more wisdom than he has and I have to share it with everyone. Which is probably true, since he was unable to even explain to me what philosophy or wisdom are. He says it's the way you view the world or your life. And how to live life to the fullest. I am going to be honest with you, just like I was with him. Philosophy and wisdom sound like a lot of bullshit to me. I mean, really, do you have to think about how you live your life? Why can't you just do it without thinking that much about it? It comes pretty naturally. I mean, you gotta plan stuff so you can make sure that you can fit everything in everyday, but what the hell else can you do? You think I planned to win at the Special

Olympics? Or planned to become a motorcycle rider? Or planned any of the funny stories I have been telling you?

Then we tried again, and he simply asked me why I got out of bed everyday so happy. Now that was a stupid question. I can't wait to get up in the morning everyday, cause I have a lot of great stuff to do. How hard is that to understand? I get up and put on my favorite clothes for the day, depending on the weather and what I am going to do. I like all my clothes cause I picked them out myself. Why did I pick them out? Because I liked them and they are comfortable. Are you following me? I go into the bathroom, brush my teeth with a cool electric toothbrush (usually a Batman or Superman model) and then use a rinse, and man, all that morning breath is gone and my mouth feels great. Finish up with a good face scrubbing and all the sleep is out of my eyes and I am ready. You know what I'm ready for? The day, man, the day. There's always stuff to do. Check my email and cruise around the Internet and watch some videos and listen to my music till my parents get up for coffee. Then we all sit around and shoot the shit for a while and get some laughs. And after that, it could be anything. We might be heading out to lunch in a few hours to my favorite hangout in Tucson, the Cup Cafe at the Hotel Congress, where everyone is funky, friendly, and cool. We sit on the patio, soak up some sun, and get drinks from Tiger, the bartender who has been there so long, that they named the bar, Tiger's Room, after him. Big neon sign with his name over the bar. And I'm telling you, the Cup Cafe is tattoo heaven–I've rubbed more tattoos on great looking women at that place than anywhere else in the world. And they have good food to boot. More stories, more laughs. Or maybe we'll go to Rocco's for pasta and pizza. Or El Minuto to go see Rosa and Terrie and Jose Luis and have some Mexican food. And I make believe I am talking Spanish with all the waiters (like Anna and Oscar) who are friends of mine and crack up when I do make-believe Spanish, though it doesn't sound that different than my English, unfortunately. But happy isn't about just having lunch. There's always more stuff to do. Maybe ride a motorcycle all the way to the Chiricahua Mountains to see these incredible rocks that are piled hundreds of feet high and takes like the whole day to ride to. Or just a quick trip for a couple of hours up to the top of Kitt Peak to see hundreds of miles over the whole desert around us. Maybe fishing at Parker Canyon Lake. Or maybe we just hang out by the pool, shoot some hoops, and get ready for an evening volleyball game or basketball game or baseball game (depending on the season). And get phone calls from friends all around the country and sometimes around the world. Or meet Kyle or Tina or Stef and Bill or any of our friends to eat a meal or do something special like go to the Desert Museum. Or do nothing at all except stay home, cause I have so many things to do at home that I can't even get to all of them. Maybe bowl on the Wii (I can get 300 almost every time with my right hand, so I'm learning with my left now–bowling around 250–275 right now lefty), or play some other video games. Maybe a little art project or something like that. Go shopping and see my buddies at the grocery or go to Casa Video and get DVD's–my dad says it's one of the last huge video stores in the country and it's great–got everything. Have big dinners that I help make. Go hang out with more friends at night, or just stay home and watch ball games or movies or TV shows.

Which brings me to the point of my responsibilities at home–it's important to be responsible for stuff at home and even that makes me happy. I'm in charge of taking the trash out, doing the laundry, helping with shopping, setting the table for meals and clearing it, reminding my parents when to take their pills cause they forget all the time. And of course, pointing out to them all the crap they are NOT doing that they are supposed to be doing, like my dad watering his garden or cleaning the pool, or putting air in the basketballs–without me, this stuff never gets done on time or properly. I even have to remind them to start dinner on time, cause they get caught up in their own crap and forget this as well. It's gotten real bad since my dad retired, cause he can barely remember what day of the week it is without me.

There's so much stuff that's gonna happen everyday that's fun, you really shouldn't be wasting your time thinking that much about it. Just get up and start doing whatever it is you want to do. See, it's not about big fancy trips to Hawaii or big cars (though I do love limos) or going to the World Series or Super Bowl, though I'm not saying those aren't fun things to do. Remember, Temple Basketball, my friends. But there are ALWAYS fun things to do right at home and in your hometown, no matter where you live, (except for the shithole on the Main Line).

So we just finished writing this part of this last chapter in the whole book and boy, it's been a long process. I looked over at my dad and he had a funny look on his face, so I asked him what was wrong.

He shrugged his shoulders. "I don't know. This isn't exactly a big bang ending."

"What the hell are you talking about? You asked me why I am always happy and I told you. What the hell else can I say?"

"You're saying it's all the little things in life that make you happy. Sounds like a fucking Disney movie or one of the 20 sitcoms you watch all the time. This is not wisdom."

"I never said it was wisdom, cause you never explained wisdom to me in a way I could understand. That's your problem."

"Fine, let's just say wisdom is sort of like one big TRUTH that explains why you are happy all the time. It's the one big THING that makes everyday a good day."

I thought about that for a few seconds. "I don't think

there are any truths like that. I'm not saying there aren't times when I get a little down, like when my back hurts or I have a bad cold. I just make sure I think about good stuff, even if there are a few tiny bad things going on. Overall, every day is a good day. That's just a fact."

My dad started getting pissed. "No, there are good days and bad days for everyone–that's part of life. But somehow, you seem to be able to avoid that. And there are very definitely major truths about life."

"Like what?"

"I don't know, like, ..., gimme a second and I'll think of one."

My dad was struggling to find a truth, so I tried to help him out. "OK, you mean a truth like Never Get in a Car with a Stranger."

He smiled. "Exactly. Now you're getting it."

"Well, what about a taxi cab?"

He stared straight into my eyes. "That's public transportation, not a stranger."

"Bullshit. That taxi driver is a total stranger and he could drive you to an empty building, tie you up, torture you, kill you and cut you up into pieces and dump the pieces into the ocean, just like all the killers in the movies and on TV."

Now my dad was getting really pissed off. "OK, that wasn't a good TRUTH."

"Well, you said it was when I told it to you."

"Well, it's not the right one I'm looking for. Gimme another second here."

"I think your whole philosophy and wisdom thing is a pile of shit, cause you can't even explain to me what they mean, you can't tell me a solid TRUTH, and you simply don't like my answer why everyday is pretty much always a good day for me. Just cause everyday isn't a good day for you, doesn't mean everyday can't be a good day for me. Now doesn't that sound pretty stupid?"

"That's my whole point. I want you to explain why your everyday is good and most everyone else's isn't."

"How the hell do I know why everyone else's every day isn't good for them? That's not my problem. That's everyone else's problem. Dad, I know you are a smart guy, but you are not getting this at all."

"No, you are not getting it, Shane. We need to sum up a very important point here about your life. It's the end of the book and it needs a real bang of an ending."

And I looked at him straight in the eye as I stood up. "Writing this book was your idea, not mine. I just did it with you because it was another fun thing to do. Get it? Just another part of why everyday is a fun day."

"So you didn't want to do it?"

"You know, dad, sometimes you are an idiot. I just told you why all my days are good days and you just don't like my answer. And you know what? You are starting to make this day and this book writing less fun for me right now."

His face started getting red. "Oh, really?"

And as I started to walk away, I just said, "I'm done. Finish the fucking ending yourself."

And as I was walking away, I smiled and laughed, because my dad had just made my day even a little funnier and he didn't even know why.

CPSIA information can be obtained
at www.ICGtesting.com
Printed in the USA
LVOW13s0632100117
520384LV00008B/112/P